Chemistry for the Grammar Stage

Teacher Guide

Chemistry for the Grammar Stage Teacher Guide

Updated Edition (Third Printing 2020)
Copyright @ Elemental Science, Inc.
Email: support@elementalscience.com

ISBN# 978-1-935614-48-7

Printed in the USA for worldwide distribution

For more copies write to:
Elemental Science
PO Box 79
Niceville, FL 32588
support@elementalscience.com

Copyright Policy

Chemistry for the Grammar Stage
Table of Contents

Chemistry for the Grammar Stage
Introduction to the Updated Edition

Since writing the first edition of *Chemistry for the Grammar Stage,* I have co-authored *Success in Science: A Manual for Excellence in Science Education* with Bradley Hudson. The purpose of this updated edition was to re-align this program with our research. It now reflects the components of the Classic Method of elementary science instruction suggested in the book. This method is loosely based on the ideas for classical science education that are laid out in *The Well-trained Mind: A Guide to Classical Education at Home* by Jessie Wise and Susan Wise Bauer.

In *Success in Science,* we compare the elementary student to an empty bucket that is waiting to be filled with meaningful information. My goal in writing this curriculum was to provide you with tools to give your elementary student exposure to the topics of atoms, elements, the periodic table and other chemical principles, thus building a knowledge base for future studies. For this reason, I have included weekly scientific demonstrations, reading suggestions, notebooking assignments, and additional activities.

This program is designed to be used during the elementary years, specifically 2nd through 5th grade. It includes a buffet of options that can be completed in either two days or five days each. Alternatively, if you desire, you could set aside an hour a week to be your science day in which you do all the readings, narrations, and activities planned for the week. Please feel free to act as the student's scribe as you complete the narration pages and lab reports.

Student Workbook (SW)

This teacher's guide is designed to work in conjunction with the *Chemistry for the Grammar Stage Student Workbook.* This workbook is sold separately, but it is critical to the success of this program. It contains all the pages you will need to complete the narrations, lab reports, and multi-week projects. The student workbook gives the students the ability to create a lasting memory of their first journey through chemistry.

Scientific Demonstrations

The scientific demonstrations scheduled in the guide generally use easy-to-find materials and tie into what is being studied. Each one has a corresponding lab report in the student workbook. At this age, you will be the driving force behind these demonstrations, meaning that you will be the one in control, and the student will be watching and participating when necessary. These demonstrations are designed to give them a beginners' look at the scientific method and how scientific tests work. It is not necessary to ask the students to predict the outcome of the demonstration since they have no knowledge base to determine what the answer should be. However, if the students enjoy predicting or they are able to tell you what will happen, please feel free to let them do so.

Each lab report includes four sections:
1. The "Our Tools" section is for the materials that were used during the demonstration.

2. The "Our Method" section is for a brief description of what was done during the scientific demonstration. This should be in the students' words.
3. The "Our Outcome" section is for what the students observed during the demonstration.
4. The "Our Insight" section is for what the students learned from the scientific demonstration.

Any time you see a box for a picture on the lab report, you can have the students draw what happened, or you can take a picture of the demonstration and glue it in the box. For younger students, I recommend that you do most (if not all) the writing for them on the lab reports.

Science-oriented Books

The science-oriented books section includes reading assignments from encyclopedias, discussion questions, and additional books for every lesson. Each reading assignment should be read with the students, or if they are capable, have them read the assignments on their own. After the reading assignment is completed, discuss the topic with the students using the provided discussion questions. These questions are meant to help the students begin to gather their thoughts in preparation for giving a narration.

In this edition of *Chemistry for the Grammar Stage,* I have also included a list of additional books for you to choose from each week. They are meant to be checked out from the library, and are not necessary to the success of this program. The list is there in case you decide that you would like to dig a little deeper into the topics. I have done my best to choose in-print, widely available books, but since every library is different, the books listed may not be available in your area. If that is the case, simply look up the topic in your local card catalog.

Notebooking

For the notebooking component, you will ask the students to narrate what they have learned from the science-oriented books. They should add their narration to their student workbook. For younger students, I recommend that you have them dictate what they have learned to you and then you write this into their student workbook. You can also have the students copy their narration into the workbook. You should expect three to four sentences from a third- or fourth- grade student.

Next, have the students color the provided picture on the narration page. All the pages and pictures you need are included in the student workbook. I suggest that you read over these pages monthly so that the students get a review of what they have been learning. I have also included optional lapbook assignments in case your students prefer to use lapbooks over notebooking.

Finally, go over the vocabulary with the students and enter it into their glossary at the rear of the student workbook. You can write this for them, have them copy the definition, or dictate the definition to the students. If you choose to have the students look up the definitions, I have included a glossary of the terms in this program in the Appendix on pp. 192-195.

Multi-week Projects and Activities

This guide includes ideas for multi-week projects and additional activities that coordinate with each lesson. The pages and pictures needed for the multi-week projects are included in the student workbook, while the directions for creating the projects are found in this guide. The additional activities include crafts and other activities that can enhance the students' learning time. There are no sheets to record these additional activities in the student workbook. However, I have included a project record sheet template on pg. 198 of the Appendix of this guide.

Memorization

The elementary student is very capable of receiving and memorizing information. With this in mind, I recommend that you capitalize on this fact by having your students memorize the included vocabulary and basic facts related to chemistry. A list of simple poems that you can use to help them memorize the characteristics of atoms, molecules, and more is included on the unit overview sheet for each unit. Remember that these poems are included as a resource for you to augment students' learning experience and are not required to use this program successfully.

Possible Schedules

I have written this updated edition to contain a buffet of activities that you can choose from when guiding the students through their first look at chemistry. This gives you, the teacher, complete freedom in what you would like to utilize to present and explore the concepts each week. However, I have also included two potential schedules for you to give an idea of how you could schedule each week. You can choose to use these as your guide or create your own. I have included two schedule templates on pp. 199-200 of the Appendix of this guide for you to use. Please note that the older spine options are primary on the schedule and younger spine options are in parenthesis.

Quizzes

We have also created a set of weekly quizzes to use with this program, which can be found at the back of the student workbook. Although these quizzes are not essential, they are helpful in assessing how much the students are retaining. You can also use the quizzes as a review of what the students have studied by giving the quiz orally or by having the students fill each quiz out with the assistance of their workbooks. The correct answers for the quizzes are included at the end of each week in this guide.

Coordinating Products

The following products by Elemental Science coordinate with this program. These eBooks are available separately through our website or with a combo package.

- 🖎 *Chemistry for the Grammar Stage Lapbooking Templates* — We have designed templates for seven lapbooks to coordinate with *Chemistry for the Grammar Stage*. You can use these lapbooks as a means of review or in place of the student workbook. The directions for using these templates are found in this guide under the notebooking section.

↳ ***Chemistry for the Grammar Stage Coloring Pages*** — We have prepared coloring pages to coordinate with almost every *Chemistry for the Grammar Stage*. Each page has a key fact about the topic along with a large picture to color.

Helpful Articles

Our goal as a company is to provide you with the information you need to be successful in your quest to educate your student in the sciences at home. This is the main reason we share tips and tools for homeschool science education on our blogs. As you prepare to guide your students through this program, you may find the following articles helpful:

↳ ***Classical Science Curriculum for the Grammar Stage Student*** — This article explains the goals of grammar stage science and demonstrates how classical educators can utilize the tools they have at their disposal to reach these goals.

   ⌨ http://elementalblogging.com/classical-science-curriculum-grammar/

↳ ***Scientific Demonstrations vs. Experiments*** — This article shares about these two types of scientific tests and points out how to use scientific demonstrations or experiments in your homeschool.

   ⌨ http://elementalscience.com/blogs/news/89905795-scientific-demonstrations-or-experiments

↳ ***What is notebooking?*** — This article clarifies what notebooking is and describes how this method can be a beneficial addition to your homeschool.

   ⌨ https://elementalscience.com/blogs/news/what-is-notebooking

Additional Resources

The following page contains quick links to the activities suggested in this guide along with several helpful downloads:

   ⌨ https://elementalscience.com/blogs/resources/cgs

Final Thoughts

As the author and publisher of this curriculum, I encourage you to contact us with any questions or problems that you might have concerning *Chemistry for the Grammar Stage* at support@ elementalscience.com. We will be more than happy to answer them as soon as we are able. You may also get additional help at our yahoo group (http://groups.yahoo.com/group/elemental_science/). I hope that you enjoy *Chemistry for the Grammar Stage*!

Required Book List

The following books are scheduled for use in this guide. You will need to purchase them or find a suitable substitute to complete this program.

Encyclopedias

All Units (Choose **one** age-appropriate option.)

📖 *Usborne Science Encyclopedia (best for 3rd through 5th grade)* **OR** *Basher Science Chemistry (best for 1st through 3rd grade)*

Periodic Table Unit (Choose **one** age-appropriate option.)

📖 *Scholastic's The Periodic Table (best for 3rd through 5th grade)* **OR** *Basher Science The Periodic Table (best for 1st through 3rd grade)*
(**Note**—There is not a great deal of material out there for each individual element of the periodic table. If you find your student would like more, I suggest trying to find a copy of *Fizz, Bubble, Flash* or Theodore Gray's *Elements: A Visual Exploration of Every Known Atom in the Universe*.)

Scientist Studies (You can also choose another option based on what your library offers.)

Louis Pasteur (Week 4 of the Mixtures Unit)
📖 *Pasteur's Fight Against Microbes by Beverly Birch and Christian Birmingham*

Marie Curie (Week 4 of the Acids and Bases Unit)
📖 *Marie Curie's Search for Radium by Beverly Birch and Christian Birmingham*

Scientific Demonstration Books

You will need the following book to complete the scientific demonstrations in this program.

📖 *Janice VanCleave's Chemistry for Every Kid*

Additional Books Listed by Week

The books listed below are completely optional! They are not required to complete this program. Instead, this list is merely a suggestion of the additional books that are available to enhance your studies. This list is by no means exhaustive.

Atoms and Molecules Unit

Atoms and Molecules Week 1
📖 *What Are Atoms? (Rookie Read-About Science)* by Lisa Trumbauer
📖 *Atoms and Molecules (Building Blocks of Matter)* by Richard and Louise Spilsbury
📖 *Atoms (Simply Science)* by Melissa Stewart

Atoms and Molecules Week 2
📖 *Atoms and Molecules (Building Blocks of Matter)* by Richard and Louise Spilsbury

📖 *Atoms and Molecules (Why Chemistry Matters)* by Molly Aloian

📖 *Atoms and Molecules (My Science Library)* by Tracy Nelson Maurer

Atoms and Molecules Week 3

📖 *Air Is All Around You (Let's-Read-and-Find... Science 1)* by Franklyn M. Branley

📖 *Air: Outside, Inside, and All Around (Amazing Science)* by Darlene R. Stille

Atoms and Molecules Week 4

📖 *Water, Water Everywhere (Reading Rainbow Book)* by Cynthia Overbeck Bix

📖 *Water* by Frank Asch

📖 *Water: Up, Down, and All Around (Amazing Science)* by Natalie M. Rosinsky

Periodic Table Unit

Periodic Table Week 1

📖 *The Elements (True Books)* by Matt Mullins

📖 *Elements and Compounds (Building Blocks of Matter)* by Louise and Richard Spilsbury

📖 *The Mystery of the Periodic Table (Living History Library)* by Benjamin D. Wiker, Jeanne Bendick and Theodore Schluenderfritz

📖 *The Periodic Table (True Books: Elements)* by Salvatore Tocci

Periodic Table Week 2

📖 *The Alkali Metals: Lithium, Sodium, Potassium, Rubidium, Cesium, Francium (Understanding the Elements of the Periodic Table)* by Kristi Lew

📖 *Hydrogen and the Noble Gases (True Books: Elements)* by Salvatore Tocci

📖 *Hydrogen: Running on Water (Energy Revolution)* by Niki Walker

📖 *Sodium (Elements)* by Anne O'Daly

📖 *Sodium (True Books: Elements)* by Salvatore Tocci

Periodic Table Week 3

📖 *The Alkaline Earth Metals: Beryllium, Magnesium, Calcium, Strontium, Barium, Radium (Understanding the Elements of the Periodic Table)* by Bridget Heos

📖 *Calcium (True Books: Elements)* by Salvatore Tocci

📖 *Magnesium (The Elements)* by Colin Uttley

Periodic Table Week 4

📖 *The Transition Elements: The 37 Transition Metals (Understanding the Elements of the Periodic Table)* by Mary-Lane Kamberg

📖 *Iron (Elements)* by Giles Sparrow

📖 *Copper (The Elements)* by Richard Beatty

Periodic Table Week 5

📖 *The Boron Elements: Boron, Aluminum, Gallium, Indium, Thallium (Understanding the Elements of the Periodic Table)* by Heather Hasan

📖 *Aluminum* by Heather Hasan

📖 *Boron (Elements)* by Richard Beatty

Periodic Table Week 6
- *The Carbon Elements: Carbon, Silicon, Germanium, Tin, Lead (Understanding the Elements of the Periodic Table)* by Brian Belval
- *Carbon* by Linda Saucerman
- *Carbon (True Books: Elements)* by Salvatore Tocci
- *Tin (True Books: Elements)* by Salvatore Tocci
- *The Invention of the Silicon Chip: A Revolution in Daily Life* by Windsor Chorlton

Periodic Table Week 7
- *The Nitrogen Elements (Understanding the Elements of the Periodic Table)* by Greg Roza
- *Nitrogen (True Books: Elements)* by Salvatore Tocci
- *Nitrogen* by Heather Hasan
- *Phosphorus (Elements)* by Richard Beatty

Periodic Table Week 8
- *The Oxygen Elements: Oxygen, Sulfur, Selenium, Tellurium, Polonium (Understanding the Elements of the Periodic Table)* by Laura La Bella
- *Nonmetals (Material Matters/Freestyle Express)* by Carol Baldwin
- *Oxygen (True Books: Elements)* by Salvatore Tocci
- *Sulfur (The Elements)* by Richard Beatty

Periodic Table Week 9
- *Fluorine (Understanding the Elements of the Periodic Table)* by Heather Hasan
- *The Elements: Iodine* by Leon Gray
- *Iodine (Understanding the Elements of the Periodic Table)* by Kristi Lew

Periodic Table Week 10
- *Hydrogen and the Noble Gases (True Books: Elements)* by Salvatore Tocci
- *Krypton (Understanding the Elements of the Periodic Table)* by Janey Levy

Periodic Table Week 11
- *The Lanthanides (Elements)* by Richard Beatty

Periodic Table Week 12
- *Radioactive Elements* by Tom Jackson
- *The 15 Lanthanides and the 15 Actinides (Understanding the Elements of the Periodic Table)* by Kristi Lew

Physical Changes Unit

Physical Changes Week 1
- *What Is the World Made Of? All About Solids, Liquids, and Gases (Let's-Read-and-Find... Science, Stage 2)* by Kathleen Weidner Zoehfeld and Paul Meisel
- *Solids, Liquids, And Gases (Rookie Read-About Science)* by Ginger Garrett
- *States of Matter: A Question and Answer Book* by Bayrock, Fiona, McMullen and Anne

Physical Changes Week 2
- *How Water Changes (Weekly Reader: Science)* by Jim Mezzanotte

- *Solids (States of Matter)* by Jim Mezzanotte
- *Liquids (States of Matter)* by Jim Mezzanotte
- *Gases (States of Matter)* Jim Mezzanotte

Physical Changes Week 3

- *What Is a Liquid?* (First Step Nonfiction, States of Matter) by Jennifer Boothroyd
- *How Do You Measure Liquids?* (A+ Books: Measure It!) by Thomas K. Adamson
- *Saving Water: The Water Cycle* (Do It Yourself) by Buffy Silverman
- *Why Do Puddles Disappear?: Noticing Forms of Water* by Martha E. H. Rustad and Christine M. Schneider

Physical Changes Week 4

- *What Is a Gas? (First Step Nonfiction)* by Jennifer Boothroyd
- *It's a Gas!* by Ruth Griffin, Margaret Griffin and Pat Cupples
- *The Atmosphere: Planetary Heat Engine (Earth's Spheres)*

Chemical Changes Unit

There are no additional books for this unit, instead there are suggested videos for the topics.

Mixtures Unit

Mixtures Week 1

- *Compounds and Mixtures (Explorer Library: Science Explorer)* by Charnan Simon
- *Mixtures and Solutions (Why Chemistry Matters)* by Molly Aloian
- *Mix It Up! Solution or Mixture?* by Tracy Nelson Maurer
- *Mixtures and Solutions (Building Blocks of Matter)* by Richard Spilsbury and Louise Spilsbury

Mixtures Week 2

- *Mixing and Separating (Changing Materials)* by Chris Oxlade
- *Mixtures and Compounds (Internet-linked Library of Science)* by Alastair Smith and P. Clarke

Mixtures Week 3

- *Crystals (Rocks and Minerals)* by Connor Dayton
- *Growing Crystals* by Ann O Squire
- *What Are Crystals? (Let's Rock!)* by Molly Aloian
- *DK Eyewitness Books: Crystal & Gem* by R.F. Symes

Mixtures Week 4

- *Louis Pasteur: Founder of Modern Medicine* by John Hudson Tiner and Michael L. Denman
- *Germ Hunter: A Story about Louis Pasteur* by Elaine Marie Alphin and Elaine Verstraete
- *Louis Pasteur and the Fight Against Germs: Life Science* by Lisa Zamosky
- *Louis Pasteur: The Father of Microbiology* by Stephen Feinstein

Acids and Bases Unit

Acids and Bases Week 1

- 📖 *Acids and Bases (Why Chemistry Matters)* by Lynnette Brent
- 📖 *Acids & Bases (Material Matters)* by Carol Baldwin
- 📖 *Acids and Bases (Chemicals in Action)* by Chris Oxlade

Acids and Bases Week 2

- 📖 There are no additional books for this unit, instead there are suggested videos for the topics.

Acids and Bases Week 3

- 📖 *From Sea to Salt (Start to Finish, Second Series)* by Lisa Owings
- 📖 *The Story of Salt* by Mark Kurlansky and S. D. Schindler

Acids and Bases Week 4

- 📖 *Who Was Marie Curie?* by Megan Stine and Nancy Harrison
- 📖 *DK Biography: Marie Curie* by DK
- 📖 *Marie Curie (Giants of Science)* by Kathleen Krull
- 📖 *World History Biographies: Marie Curie: The Woman Who Changed the Course of Science* by Philip Steele

Organic Chemistry Unit

Organic Chemistry Week 1

- 📖 *Why We Need Fats (Science of Nutrition)* by Molly Aloian
- 📖 *Fats for a Healthy Body: For a Healthy Body (Body Needs)* by Heinemann

Organic Chemistry Week 2

- 📖 There are no additional books for this unit, instead there are suggested videos for the topics.

Organic Chemistry Week 3

- 📖 *Oil Spill! (Let's-Read-and-Find-Out Science)* by Melvin Berger and Paul Mirocha
- 📖 *Using Coal, Oil, and Gas (Exploring Earth's Resources)* by Sharon Katz Cooper
- 📖 *From Oil to Gas (Start to Finish, Second Series: Everyday Products)* by Shannon Zemlicka
- 📖 *Finding Out About Coal, Oil, and Natural Gas* by Matt Doeden

Organic Chemistry Week 4

- 📖 *Plastic (Everyday Materials)* by Andrew Langley
- 📖 *Plastic, Ahoy!: Investigating the Great Pacific Garbage Patch* by Patricia Newman and Annie Crawley
- 📖 *The Adventures of a Plastic Bottle: A Story About Recycling (Little Green Books)* by Alison Inches and Pete Whitehead
- 📖 *From Plastic to Soccer Ball (Start to Finish: Sports Gear)* by Robin Nelson

Supplies Needed by Week

Atoms and Molecules Unit

Week	Supplies needed
1	4 Pipe cleaners, Round beads in three different colors, at least 3 of each color
2	Jar with lid, Water, Food Coloring
3	Empty plastic bread sack
4	Cup, Water, Salt

Periodic Table Unit

Week	Supplies needed
1	Legos - a variety of colors and sizes, Paper, Pen
2	Metal can, Thermometer, Table salt, Crushed ice
3	Epsom salts, Ammonia, Clear jar
4	3 Tea bags, 4 Different types of juice, Clear plastic glasses, Tablespoon
5	Alum powder, Ammonia, Clear jar
6	Limewater (Powdered lime, Water, Jar with lid), Straw, Cup
7	Can of dark cola soda, Glass, Dirty Pennies
8	Apple, Vitamin C tablet
9	Iodine swab, Notebook paper, Lemon juice, Cup, Paint brush
10	Helium-filled balloon, Scissors
11	3 Cups, 3 Pencils, 3 Clear liquids (i.e., water, alcohol, and corn syrup)
12	Bite-sized food, such as raisins or cereal puffs, Timer

Physical Changes Unit

Week	Supplies needed
1	3 Balloons, Ice, Water
2	Orange Juice, Cup
3	3 Toothpicks, Dish soap, Bowl
4	2-Liter soda bottle, Quarter, Water

Supplies Needed by Week

Chemical Changes Unit

Week	Supplies needed
1	Wax paper, Toothpicks, Eyedroppers, Water
2	Saucer, Paper towel, Vinegar, Pennies
3	Bread, Iodine, Eyedropper, Wax paper
4	Apple, Lemon juice

Mixtures Unit

Week	Supplies needed
1	Clear glass, Toothpick, Powdered fruit drink, Water
2	Black water soluble pen, Coffee filter, Saucer, Paper clip
3	Glass jar, Pencil, Pipe cleaners, Borax, Hot water
4	*No supplies needed.*

Acids and Bases Unit

Week	Supplies needed
Unit Prep*	Strainer, Glass jar, Distilled water, Purple Cabbage, Coffee filters, Cookie sheet, Bowl, Scissors, Plastic bag
1	Lemonade, Cabbage indicator, Glass, Tablespoon
2	Cabbage paper, Paper, Eyedroppers, Vinegar, Ammonia, Jars
3	Vinegar, Baking soda, Water, Cabbage juice, Cabbage paper, 2 Clear cups, Eyedropper
4	*No supplies needed.*

Organic Chemistry Unit

Week	Supplies needed
1	Construction paper, 6 Types of food (Cheese, Fruit, Yogurt, Chips, Muffin, Vegetable), Marker
2	Jar with lid, Rubbing alcohol, Cloves
3	Large clear glass bowl, Vegetable Oil, Water, Plastic spoon, Cotton balls, Polyester felt square
4	Vegetable oil, Cornstarch, Water, Food coloring, Plastic bag, Eyedropper

Chemistry for the Grammar Stage

Atoms and Molecules Unit

Atoms and Molecules Unit Overview
(4 weeks)

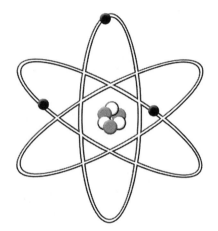

Books Scheduled

Encyclopedias

📖 *Basher Science Chemistry*

OR

📖 *Usborne Science Encyclopedia*

Scientific Demonstrations Book

📖 *JVC Chemistry for Every Kid*

Sequence for Study

✎ Week 1: Atoms
✎ Week 2: Molecules
✎ Week 3: Air
✎ Week 4: Water

Atoms and Molecules Poem to Memorize

Atoms and Molecules

Atoms are the stuff that makes what we got,
Forming molecules found in your teapot.
Inside the atom are three little specks,
Subatomic particles kept in check.
At the center are neutrons and protons,
Spinning around in shells are electrons.
All three parts balanced in equality,
Gives the atom its own frivolity.
One or more atoms uniquely combine,
Creating a molecular design.
These molecules we can breathe, eat, and wear.
Meet them every day in water and air.

Supplies Needed for the Unit

Week	Supplies needed
1	4 Pipe cleaners, Round beads in three different colors, at least 3 of each color
2	Jar with lid, Water, Food Coloring

3	Empty plastic bread sack
4	Cup, Water, Salt

Unit Vocabulary

1. **Electron** – A negatively charged particle in an atom.
2. **Proton** – A positively charged particle in an atom.
3. **Neutron** – A neutral particle in an atom.
4. **Isotope** – An atom that has a different number of neutrons and so has a different mass number from the other atoms of an element.
5. **Electron Shell** – The region around an atom's nucleus in which a certain amount of electrons can reside.
6. **Molecule** – A substance made up of two or more atoms that are chemically bonded.
7. **Air** – A mixture of gases that form a protective layer around the Earth.
8. **Hard Water** – Water that contains a lot of dissolved minerals.

Week 1: Atoms Lesson Plans

Scientific Demonstration: Model Atom

Supplies Needed
- ✓ 4 Pipe cleaners
- ✓ Round beads in three different colors, at least 3 of each color

Purpose
This demonstration is meant to help the students see what an atom looks like.

Instructions
1. Have the students select which beads will be electrons, protons, and neutrons.
2. Next, have them string three protons beads and three neutrons beads on one of the pipe cleaners, alternating between the two. Once done, have the students wrap the this portion of the pipe cleaner into a ball to form a nucleus, leaving a straight end to connect to the electron rings they will make in the next step.
3. Then, have the students place one electron bead on a pipe cleaner and twist the pipe cleaner closed to form a ring. Repeat this process two more times, so that they have 3 electron rings.
4. Finally, fit the rings inside each other and then hang the nucleus ball in the center, using the pipe cleaner tail left in step two to attach the nucleus and hold the rings together. (*See image for reference.*)
5. Have the students take a picture of their atoms and complete the Lab Report on SW pg. 9.

Take it Further
Have the students repeat the process, only this time have them create an isotope by adding or removing one of the neutrons.

Science-Oriented Books

Reading Assignments
- 📖 *Basher Science Chemistry pg. 26 Atom, pg. 28 Isotope*
- 📖 *Usborne Science Encyclopedia pp. 10–11 Atomic Structure, pg 13 Isotopes and Atomic Theory*

(Optional) Additional topics to explore this week: *Basher Science Chemistry pg. 30 (Ions)*

Discussion Questions
After reading the selected pages, ask the following questions for your discussion time.

Subatomic Particles
? What are the three subatomic particles?

? What are their charges?

Atoms

? What is an atom?

? What does an atom look like?

Isotope

? What is an isotope?

(Optional) Additional Books

- 📖 *What Are Atoms? (Rookie Read-About Science)* by Lisa Trumbauer
- 📖 *Atoms and Molecules (Building Blocks of Matter)* by Richard and Louise Spilsbury
- 📖 *Atoms (Simply Science)* by Melissa Stewart

Notebooking

Writing Assignments

☐ **Narration Page –** Have the students dictate, copy, or write one to four sentences on subatomic particles, atoms, and isotopes on SW pg. 8. For example, for this week the students could dictate, copy, or write the following for subatomic particles:

> *There are three subatomic particles – protons, neutrons, and electrons.*
> *Protons and neutrons live in the nucleus of an atom.*
> *Electrons fly around the nucleus.*
> *Protons are positively charged and electrons are negatively charged.*

☐ **(Optional) Lapbook –** Have the students begin the Atoms and Molecules lapbook by cutting out and coloring the cover on pg. 6.

☐ **(Optional) Lapbook –** Have the students complete the Atoms wheel-book on pg. 7 of *Chemistry for the Grammar Stage Lapbooking Templates*. Have them cut along the solid lines, punch a hole in the center, and use a brad fastener to fasten the two circles together. Have the students write their electron narration to the left of the picture, their proton narration above the picture, and their neutron narration to the right of the picture. Finally, have them glue their mini-book into the lapbook.

☐ **(Optional) Lapbook –** Have the students complete the Isotopes shutterfold book on pg. 8 of *Chemistry for the Grammar Stage Lapbooking Templates*. Have them cut out and fold the template. Have the students color the pictures on the cover. Have them write their narration about the isotopes inside the mini-book. Then, have them glue the mini-book into the lapbook.

Vocabulary

The following definitions are a guide. The students' definitions do not need to match word for word.

- ✎ **Electron –** A negatively charged particle in an atom. (SW pg. 107)
- ✎ **Proton –** A positively charged particle in an atom. (SW pg. 113)
- ✎ **Neutron –** A neutral particle in an atom. (SW pg. 111)

✐ **Isotope –** An atom that has a different number of neutrons and so has a different mass number from the other atoms of an element. (SW pg. 110)

Multi-week Projects and Activities

Unit Project

✂ **Atoms and Molecules Poster –** Over this unit, the students will create a poster about atoms and molecules, giving them a visual representation of the basics of chemistry. The poster will have three main sections - sub atomic particles, atoms and elements, and molecules. This week, have the students add the electron, proton, and neutron to the "subatomic particle" section. They can draw or paint circles with charges for each or use pompoms. Then, have them use the same circles or pompoms to represent an atom on the left-hand side of the "atoms and elements" section. (*See the included image.*) After the students finish the artwork, have them write a sentence or two about each subatomic particle. (*This has been done for you in the SW on pg. 6.*)

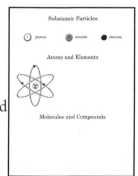

Projects for this Week

✂ **Coloring Pages –** Have the students color the following pages from *Chemistry for the Grammar Stage Coloring Pages*: Atoms pg. 5, Isotopes pg. 6.

✂ **Subatomic Particles –** Make some subatomic cookies with your students using a sugar cookie, white icing, and three different colors of M&M's. See the following website for directions:

🖰 http://technoprairie.blogspot.com/2009/02/atomic-cookies.html

✂ **Atoms –** Have the students make a fruit atom model. In the center of a plate, have the students build a mound of raspberries and grapes for the protons and neutrons in the nucleus. Then, they can roll blueberries in a circle around the nucleus for the electrons. Once, they are done playing, let the students gobble their atoms up!

✂ **Isotopes –** Have the students play an atoms and isotopes game. You can get directions for this game from the following blog post:

🖰 http://elementalscience.com/blogs/science-activities/60317571-free-chemistry-game

Memorization

📢 This week, begin working on memorizing the *Atoms and Molecules* poem. (SW pg. 118)

Quiz

Weekly Quiz

🖋 "Atoms and Molecules Unit Week 1 Quiz" on SW pg. Q-5.

Quiz Answers

1. Positive, Negative, Neutral
2. Protons, Neutrons, Electrons
3. True
4. Answers will vary

Possible Schedules for Week 1

Two Days a Week Schedule	
Day 1	**Day 2**
❑ Read about Atomic Structure (Atom) ❑ Add information about subatomic particles and atoms to the students' Narration Page ❑ Do the Scientific Demonstration: Atom Model ❑ Work on memorizing the *Atoms and Molecules* poem ❑ Define electron, proton, and neutron	❑ Read about Isotopes and Atomic Theory (Isotope) ❑ Add information about isotopes to the students' Narration Page ❑ Define isotope ❑ Work on the Atoms and Molecules Poster ❑ Give Atoms and Molecules Week 1 quiz

Five Days a Week Schedule				
Day 1	**Day 2**	**Day 3**	**Day 4**	**Day 5**
❑ Do the Scientific Demonstration: Atom Model ❑ Define electron, proton, and neutron ❑ Choose one or more of the additional books to read from this week	❑ Read about Atomic Structure - sections on pg. 10 (Atom) ❑ Add information about subatomic particles and atoms to the students' Narration Page ❑ Complete the Subatomic Particles Project	❑ Review the pages about Atomic Structure - sections on pg. 11 (Atom) ❑ Add information about atoms to the students' Narration Page ❑ Complete the Atoms Project	❑ Read about Isotopes and Atomic Theory (Isotope) ❑ Add information about isotopes to the students' Narration Page ❑ Complete the Isotopes Project ❑ Define isotope	❑ Give Atoms and Molecules Week 1 quiz ❑ Work on the Atoms and Molecules Poster
All Week Long				
❑ Work on memorizing the *Atoms and Molecules* poem				

Week 2: Molecules Lesson Plans

Scientific Demonstration: Unseen Movement

Supplies Needed
- ✓ Jar with lid
- ✓ Water
- ✓ Food Coloring

Purpose
This demonstration is meant to help the students see how molecules move.

Instructions and Explanation
The instructions and explanation for this scientific demonstration are found on pp. 12-13 of *Janice VanCleave's Chemistry for Every Kid.* Have the students complete the Lab Report on SW pg. 11.

Take it Further
Have the students look at how temperature affects molecular motion by repeating the demonstration with a glass of cold and warm water. (*They should see that the food coloring molecules move much faster in the warm water.*)

Science-Oriented Books

Reading Assignments
- 📖 *Basher Science Chemistry pg. 32 Molecules* (**Note** - *The information for the electron shells is not in this resource. You will need to share with your students that the first shell can contain 2 electrons, the second shell can contain 8 electrons, and the third shell generally carries 8 electrons, but can carry as many as 18 for certain atoms.*)
- 📖 *Usborne Science Encyclopedia pp. 14-15 Molecules*
- 📖 *"Polar and Nonpolar" on Appendix pg. 188*
- 📖 **Molecules or Compounds** — Molecules are formed when two or more atoms join together. Compounds are formed when two or more elements join together. For example H_2 (hydrogen gas) is a molecule because two atoms of hydrogen are joined together. However, since there is only one type of element present, H_2 is not a compound. On the other hand, H_2O (water) is a molecule because the three atoms, one oxygen atom and two hydrogen atoms, have been joined together to form it. It is also a compound because it contains two different elements, hydrogen and oxygen. So, all compounds are molecules, but not all molecules are compounds.

(Optional) Additional topics to explore this week: *Basher Chem pg. 34 (Giant Molecule)*

Discussion Questions
After reading the selected pages, ask the following questions for your discussion time.

Electron Shells

? How many electrons fit in the first shell?

? How many electrons fit in the second shell?

? How many electrons fit in the third shell?

Molecule

? What is a molecule?

? What are some examples of molecules?

? What are two ways (models) of showing molecules?

Nonpolar and Polar

? What is a nonpolar molecule?

? What is a polar molecule?

(Optional) Additional Books

- *Atoms and Molecules (Building Blocks of Matter)* by Richard and Louise Spilsbury
- *Atoms and Molecules (Why Chemistry Matters)* by Molly Aloian
- *Atoms and Molecules (My Science Library)* by Tracy Nelson Maurer

Notebooking

Writing Assignments

- ☐ **Narration Page –** Have the students dictate, copy, or write one to four sentences on electron shells, molecules, and nonpolar and polar molecules on SW pg. 10.
- ☐ **(Optional) Lapbook –** Have the students work on the Electron Shell Diagram on pg. 8 of *Chemistry for the Grammar Stage Lapbooking Templates*. Have the students cut out the sheet, color the shells different colors, and add the information they have learned about how many electrons the first three shells can carry. Finally, have them glue their sheets into their lapbooks.
- ☐ **(Optional) Lapbook –** Have the students work on the Molecules tab-book on pg. 9 of *Chemistry for the Grammar Stage Lapbooking Templates*. Have the students write the definition of a molecule on the definition page and then add any molecules they have learned about to the samples page. Set the mini-book aside and save it for next week.

Vocabulary

The following definitions are a guide. The students' definitions do not need to match word for word.

- ✍ **Electron Shell –** The region around an atom's nucleus in which a certain amount of electrons can reside. (SW pg. 107)
- ✍ **Molecule –** A substance made up of two or more atoms that are chemically bonded. (SW pg. 111)

Multi-week Projects and Activities

Unit Project

✂ **Atoms and Molecules Poster –** This week, have the students add a picture of molecules to the "molecules and compounds" section of their poster. This can be as simple as the written formula for water (H_2O) or methane (CH_4) or as complicated as a drawing of one of the molecules they saw in their readings. After the students finish the artwork, have them write a sentence or two about molecules.

Projects for this Week

✂ **Coloring Pages –** Have the students color the following pages from *Chemistry for the Grammar Stage Coloring Pages*: Electron Shells pg. 7, Molecules pg. 8, Polar and Nonpolar Molecules pg. 9.

✂ **Electron Shells –** Have the students play the atoms and isotopes game again, only this time focus on reviewing how many electrons are in each shell. If you did not play this last week, you can get directions for this game from the following blog post:

👆 http://elementalscience.com/blogs/science-activities/60317571-free-chemistry-game

✂ **Molecules –** Have the students make molecules models out of LEGOS using the examples from the following pin:

👆 https://www.pinterest.com/pin/192036371586132562/

✂ **Polar and Nonpolar –** Have the students have a molecule race using a polar substance (water) and a nonpolar one (wax paper). Use an eyedropper to sprinkle a drop of water at the end of a wax paper sheet in front of each student. Then, give each of the students a straw and have them blow through it to move their water "molecule" drop to the finish line at the other end of the wax paper.

Memorization

🗣 This week, continue working on memorizing the *Atoms and Molecules* poem. (SW pg. 118)

Quiz

Weekly Quiz

🖋 "Atoms and Molecules Unit Week 2 Quiz" on SW pg. Q-6.

Quiz Answers

1. 2, 8, 8 to 18
2. False (*A molecule can be made up of more than one element.*)
3. Charged, Not charged
4. Answers will vary

Possible Schedules for Week 2

Two Days a Week Schedule	
Day 1	**Day 2**
❑ Read about Molecules (Molecules)	❑ Read about Polar and Nonpolar molecules from the Appendix
❑ Add information about electron shells and molecules to the students' Narration Page	❑ Add information about polar and nonpolar molecules to the students' Narration Page
❑ Do the Scientific Demonstration: Unseen Movement	❑ Work on memorizing the *Atoms and Molecules* poem
❑ Define electron shell and molecule	❑ Give Atoms and Molecules Week 2 quiz
❑ Work on the Atoms and Molecules Poster	

Five Days a Week Schedule				
Day 1	**Day 2**	**Day 3**	**Day 4**	**Day 5**
❑ Do the Scientific Demonstration: Unseen Movement ❑ Define electron shell and molecule ❑ Choose one or more of the additional books to read from this week	❑ Read about Molecules - sections on pg. 14 ❑ Add information about electron shells and atoms to the students' Narration Page ❑ Complete the Electron Shells Project	❑ Read about Molecules - sections on pg. 15 (Molecules) ❑ Add information about molecules to the students' Narration Page ❑ Complete the Molecules Project	❑ Read about Polar and Nonpolar molecules from the Appendix ❑ Add information about polar and nonpolar to the students' Narration Page ❑ Complete the Polar and Nonpolar Project	❑ Give Atoms and Molecules Week 2 quiz ❑ Work on the Atoms and Molecules Poster
All Week Long				
❑ Work on memorizing the *Atoms and Molecules* poem				

Week 3: Air Lesson Plans

Scientific Demonstration: An Empty Sack

Supplies Needed
✓ Empty plastic bread sack

Purpose
This demonstration is meant to help the students see that air molecules occupy space

Instructions and Explanation
The instructions and explanation for this scientific demonstration are found on pp. 14-15 of *Janice VanCleave's Chemistry for Every Kid*. Have the students complete the Lab Report on SW pg. 13.

Take it Further
Have the students repeat the demonstration with different containers, such as a plastic grocery bag or a paper bag, to see how the results differ.

Science-Oriented Books

Reading Assignments
📖 *Basher Science Chemistry pg. 96 Air, pg. 110 Oxygen, pg. 112 Carbon Dioxide*
📖 *Usborne Science Encyclopedia pp. 62-63 Air*

(Optional) Additional topics to explore this week: *No additional topics scheduled.*

Discussion Questions
After reading the selected pages, ask the following questions for your discussion time.

Air
? What is air?
? What are the two main gases found in air?

Oxygen
? What is oxygen essential for?
? How do animals use oxygen?
? How do plants provide oxygen?

Carbon Dioxide
? What is carbon dioxide?
? What do plants and animals do with carbon dioxide?

(Optional) Additional Books
📖 *Air Is All Around You (Let's-Read-and-Find... Science 1)* by Franklyn M. Branley
📖 *Air: Outside, Inside, and All Around (Amazing Science)* by Darlene R. Stille

Notebooking

Writing Assignments
☐ **Narration Page –** Have the students dictate, copy, or write one to four sentences on air,

oxygen, and carbon dioxide on SW pg. 12.

- ☐ **(Optional) Lapbook** – Have the students add carbon dioxide to the samples page of their molecule tab-book. Set the mini-book aside and save it for next week.

- ☐ **(Optional) Lapbook** – Have the students complete the Air mini-book on pg. 10 of *Chemistry for the Grammar Stage Lapbooking Templates*. Have them cut out and fold the template. Have the students color the pictures on the cover. Have them write their narration about the air inside the mini-book. Then, have them glue the mini-book into the lapbook.

Vocabulary

The following definitions are a guide. The students' definitions do not need to match word for word.

- ✎ **Air** – A mixture of gases that form a protective layer around the Earth. (SW pg. 104)

Multi-week Projects and Activities

Unit Project

- ✂ **Atoms and Molecules Poster** – This week, have the students add a picture of oxygen to the "atoms and elements" section and carbon dioxide to the "molecules and compounds" section of their poster. After the students finish the artwork, have them write a sentence or two about what they have added.

Projects for this Week

- ✂ **Coloring Pages** – Have the students color the following pages from *Chemistry for the Grammar Stage Coloring Pages*: Air pg. 10.

- ✂ **Air** – Have the students play a game with air. You will need a balloon for this activity. Blow up the balloon, sharing with the students that air is what fills the balloons. Then, hit the balloon back and forth to each other. The goal of the game is to keep the balloon from touching the ground. See how many times you can go back and forth without doing so!

- ✂ **Oxygen** – Have the students see how oxygen is need for combustion. You will need a candle and a clear glass bottle for this activity. Light the candle and let it burn for a bit. Then, place the glass bottle over the candle and watch what happens. (*The candle will burn for a bit before going out. This is because it uses up all the oxygen trapped in the air in the bottle.*)

- ✂ **Carbon Dioxide** – Have the students test how carbon dioxide puts out a fire. You will need a candle, a bottle, baking soda, and vinegar. The directions for this activity can be found in the *Usborne Science Encyclopedia* on pg. 63.

Memorization

- ✤ This week, continue working on memorizing the *Atoms and Molecules* poem. (SW pg. 118)

Quiz

Weekly Quiz
- "Atoms and Molecules Unit Week 3 Quiz" on SW pg. Q-7.

Quiz Answers
1. Nitrogen, Oxygen
2. Life
3. Oxygen, Carbon dioxide, Carbon dioxide, Oxygen
4. Answers will vary

Possible Schedules for Week 3

Two Days a Week Schedule

Day 1	Day 2
❑ Read about Air - sections on pg. 62 (Air and Oxygen)	❑ Read about Air - sections on pg. 63 (Carbon Dioxide)
❑ Add information about air and oxygen to the students' Narration Page	❑ Add information about carbon dioxide to the students' Narration Page
❑ Define air	❑ Work on the Atoms and Molecules Poster
❑ Do the Scientific Demonstration: An Empty Sack	❑ Work on memorizing the *Atoms and Molecules* poem
	❑ Give Atoms and Molecules Week 3 quiz

Five Days a Week Schedule

Day 1	Day 2	Day 3	Day 4	Day 5
❑ Do the Scientific Demonstration: An Empty Sack ❑ Define air ❑ Choose one or more of the additional books to read from this week	❑ Read about Air - sections on air and gases in the air (Air) ❑ Add information about air to the students' Narration Page ❑ Complete the Air Project	❑ Read about Air - sections on separating gases and oxygen (Oxygen) ❑ Add information about oxygen to the students' Narration Page ❑ Complete the Oxygen Project	❑ Read about Air - sections on carbon dioxide and air quality (Carbon Dioxide) ❑ Add information about carbon dioxide to the students' Narration Page ❑ Complete the Carbon Dioxide Project	❑ Give Atoms and Molecules Week 3 quiz ❑ Work on the Atoms and Molecules Poster

All Week Long

❑ Work on memorizing the *Atoms and Molecules* poem

Week 4: Water Lesson Plans

Scientific Demonstration: Disappearing Salt

Supplies Needed
- ✓ Cup
- ✓ Water
- ✓ Salt

Purpose
This demonstration is meant to help the students see how water easily dissolves a substance.

Instructions
1. Fill the cup about halfway with warm water.
2. Add a teaspoon of salt and stir it around several times.
3. Have the students observe what happens and write what they see on the Lab Report on SW pg. 15.

Explanation
The students should see that the salt quickly disappears after a few stirs. This is because the water molecules have a slight charge. This slight charge allows for ionic compounds, like salt, to easily dissolve in water. For this reason, water is known as the universal solvent.

Take it Further
Have the students repeat the process using sugar to see if the results vary.

Science-Oriented Books

Reading Assignments
- 📖 *Basher Science Chemistry pg. 108 Water (**Note** – The information for hard water and solvents is not in this resource, except as a definition.)*
- 📖 *Usborne Science Encyclopedia pp. 72-73 Water*

(Optional) Additional topics to explore this week: *Usborne Science Encyclopedia pp. 74-75 Water (Sections on the Water Cycle and Pollution)*

Discussion Questions
After reading the selected pages, ask the following questions for your discussion time.

Water
- **?** What is the most abundant compound on earth?
- **?** What two elements make up water?
- **?** Why does ice float on water?

Water as a Solvent
- **?** Why is water a good solvent?

Hard Water
- **?** What makes water hard?

? What makes water soft?

(Optional) Additional Books
- 📖 *Water, Water Everywhere (Reading Rainbow Book)* by Cynthia Overbeck Bix
- 📖 *Water* by Frank Asch
- 📖 *Water: Up, Down, and All Around (Amazing Science)* by Natalie M. Rosinsky

Notebooking

Writing Assignments
- ☐ **Narration Page –** Have the students dictate, copy, or write one to four sentences on water, water as a solvent, and hard water on SW pg. 14.
- ☐ **(Optional) Lapbook –** Have the students add water to the samples page of their molecule tab-book. Set the mini-book aside and save it for next week.
- ☐ **(Optional) Lapbook –** Have the students complete the Water mini-book on pg. 11 of *Chemistry for the Grammar Stage Lapbooking Templates*. Have them cut out and fold the template. Have the students color the pictures on the cover. Have them write their narration about water inside the mini-book. Then, glue the mini-book into the lapbook.
- ☐ **(Optional) Lapbook –** Have the students finish their lapbook. Have them cut out and color the *Atoms and Molecules* poem on pg. 12 of *Chemistry for the Grammar Stage Lapbooking Templates*. Once they are done, have them glue the sheet into their lapbook.

Vocabulary
The following definitions are a guide. The students' definitions do not need to match word for word.
- ✏ **Hard Water –** Water which contains a lot of dissolved minerals. (SW pg. 109)

Multi-week Projects and Activities

Unit Project
- ✂ **Atoms and Molecules Poster –** This week, have the students add a picture of hydrogen to the "atoms and elements" section and water to the "molecules and compounds" section of their poster. After the students finish the artwork, have them write a sentence or two about what they have added.

Projects for this Week
- ✂ **Coloring Pages –** Have the students color the following pages from *Chemistry for the Grammar Stage Coloring Pages*: Water pg. 11.
- ✂ **Water –** Test whether ice is less dense than water. You will need a cup and several cubes of ice. Fill the cup two-thirds of the way full with water. Add two to three ice cubes and observe what happens.
- ✂ **Water Art –** Have the students paint with water colors! As they create their pictures, discuss the fact that they are able to paint with the colors because water is such a good solvent.

✂ **Hard water** – Make a jar of hard water and observe its sudsing capabilities. You will need Plaster of Paris, water, liquid soap, and a jar with a lid. Have the students mix 1 TBSP of Plaster of Paris with 1 cup of water in the jar. Mix well. Add several drops of liquid soap, cover, and shake the jar for about 30 seconds and observe the bubbles formed. (*The water in the jar is hard and should not create very many bubbles. If you want to compare it with soft water, repeat the activity, only this time swap use Epsom salts instead of the Plaster of Paris.*)

Memorization

🗣 This week, continue working on memorizing the *Atoms and Molecules* poem. (SW pg. 118)

Quiz

Weekly Quiz
🔖 "Atoms and Molecules Unit Week 4 Quiz" on SW pg. Q-8.

Quiz Answers
1. Water
2. More, Less
3. True
4. Answers will vary

Possible Schedules for Week 4

Two Days a Week Schedule	
Day 1	**Day 2**
❑ Read the section about Water as a Solvent on pg. 73 ❑ Add information about water as a solvent to the students' Narration Page ❑ Define hard water ❑ Do the Scientific Demonstration: Disappearing Salt	❑ Read about Water (Water) ❑ Add information about water and hard water to the students' Narration Page ❑ Work on the Atoms and Molecules Poster ❑ Work on memorizing the *Atoms and Molecules* poem ❑ Give Atoms and Molecules Week 4 quiz

Five Days a Week Schedule				
Day 1	**Day 2**	**Day 3**	**Day 4**	**Day 5**
❑ Do the Scientific Demonstration: Disappearing Salt ❑ Define hard water	❑ Read about Water - sections on pg. 72 (Water) ❑ Add information about water to the students' Narration Page ❑ Complete the Water Project	❑ Read about Water - sections on pg. 73 ❑ Add information about water as a solvent and hard water to the students' Narration Page ❑ Complete the Hard Water Project	❑ Choose one or more of the additional books to read from this week ❑ Complete the Water Art Project	❑ Give Atoms and Molecules Week 4 quiz ❑ Work on the Atoms and Molecules Poster
All Week Long				
❑ Work on memorizing the *Atoms and Molecules* poem				

Chemistry for the Grammar Stage

Periodic Table Unit

Periodic Table Unit Overview
(12 weeks)

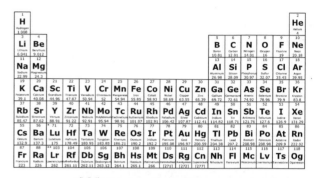

Books Scheduled

Encyclopedias

- 📖 *Basher Science Chemistry*
- 📖 *Basher Science The Periodic Table*

OR

- 📖 *Usborne Science Encyclopedia*
- 📖 *Scholastic's The Periodic Table*

Scientific Demonstrations Book

- 📖 *JVC Chemistry for Every Kid*

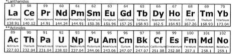

Sequence for Study

- ↻ **Week 1:** Elements and the Periodic Table
- ↻ **Week 2:** Alkali Metals
- ↻ **Week 3:** Alkaline Earth Metals
- ↻ **Week 4:** Transition Metals
- ↻ **Week 5:** Boron Elements
- ↻ **Week 6:** Carbon Elements
- ↻ **Week 7:** Nitrogen Elements
- ↻ **Week 8:** Oxygen Elements
- ↻ **Week 9:** Halogens
- ↻ **Week 10:** Noble Gases
- ↻ **Week 11:** Lanthanides
- ↻ **Week 12:** Actinides

Periodic Table Poems to Memorize

<u>The Periodic Table</u> *(Author Unknown)*
Each element has a spot on the Periodic Table,
Whether metal or gas, radioactive or stable.
You can find out its number, its symbol, its weight,
And from its position, its physical state.

Elements lined up in columns and rows,
The reason for this order, as each chemist knows,
Is that atoms are made up of still smaller bits,
(Figuring this out tested scientists' wits!)

In the nucleus, protons and neutrons are found,
And a cloud of electrons is buzzing around.

First take one proton, put in its place;
Now you have hydrogen, the simplest case.

Add two neutrons and one more proton,
And suddenly, the hydrogen's gone!
Now you have helium, quite different stuff...
You get the picture; I've said enough.

These tiny particles: they're like building blocks
That make people and buildings, flowers and rocks.
They create all of the elements we find
In everyday things of every kind!

Supplies Needed for the Unit

Week	Supplies needed
1	LEGOS - a variety of colors and sizes, Paper, Pen
2	Metal can, Thermometer, Table salt, Crushed ice
3	Epsom salts, Ammonia, Clear jar
4	3 Tea bags, 4 Different types of juice, Clear plastic glasses, Tablespoon
5	Alum powder, Ammonia, Clear jar
6	Limewater (Powdered lime, Water, Jar with lid), Straw, Cup
7	Can of dark cola soda, Glass, Dirty Pennies
8	Apple, Vitamin C tablet
9	Iodine swab, Notebook paper, Lemon juice, Cup, Paint brush
10	Helium-filled balloon, Scissors
11	3 Cups, 3 Pencils, 3 Clear liquids (i.e., water, alcohol, and corn syrup)
12	Bite-sized food, such as raisins or cereal puffs, Timer

Unit Vocabulary

1. **Atomic Number –** The number of protons in the nucleus of an atom.
2. **Atomic Mass –** The average mass number of the atoms in a sample of an element.
3. **Elements –** A substance made up of one type of atom, which cannot be broken down by chemical reaction to form a simpler substance.
4. **Chemical Symbol –** A shorthand way of representing a specific element in formulae

and equations.

5. **Periodic Table** – A systematic arrangement of the elements in order of increasing atomic number.
6. **Reactive** – The tendency of a substance to react with other substances.
7. **Metal** – The largest class of elements; they are usually shiny and solid at room temperature.
8. **Alloy** – A mixture of two or more metals or a metal and a non-metal.
9. **Metalloid** – An element that shares some of the properties of metals and nonmetals.
10. **Nonmetal** – A class of elements that can be non-shiny solids or gases.
11. **Essential Element** – An element that is essential to life on earth, such as carbon, hydrogen, nitrogen, and oxygen.
12. **Oxidation** – A chemical reaction in which a substance combines with oxygen.
13. **Ion** – An atom or group of atoms that has become charged by gaining or losing one or more electrons.
14. **Inert** – An element that is completely nonreactive.
15. **Refraction** – The bending of light as it passes through a different medium.
16. **Radioactive Decay** – The process by which a nucleus ejects particles through radiation to becoming the nucleus of a series of different elements until stability is reached.

Week 1: Elements and the Periodic Table Lesson Plans

Scientific Demonstration: Table Sorting

Supplies Needed
- ✓ LEGOS - a variety of colors and sizes (*You can also used stuffed animals, buttons, beads, or any other object with different sizes and colors if you don't have any LEGOS.*)
- ✓ Paper, Pen

Purpose
This demonstration is meant to give the students a first hand look at how the periodic table got its start.

Instructions
1. Gather the LEGOS in an unorganized pile. Draw a 4 by 6 grid on the piece of paper. (*If you are using larger objects to sort, such as stuffed animals, you can create this grid on the floor with masking tape.*)
2. Explain to the students that you are going to make a periodic table of Legos. In your table, the Legos are going to get bigger as you go down the grid and darker as you go across. (*See the included grid for visual explanation.*)

	White	Yellow	Red	Blue	Brown	Black
smallest						
largest						

3. Have the students sort the Lego by size and color onto the grid. As they sort, share with them how the periodic table in chemistry is an organized assortment of elements set up in a grid, similar to how they are sorting their Legos.
4. Have the students dictate, copy, or write one to four sentences and add a picture of their finished table on SW pg. 21.

Explanations
The point of this demonstrations is for the students to see the order that exists in the arrangement of the elements in the periodic table.

Science-Oriented Books

Reading Assignments
- ▱ *Scholastic's The Periodic Table pp. 8-9 What is an element?, pp. 14-15 The Periodic Table*
- ▱ *Basher Science Periodic Table pg. 18 Elements, pg. 6 Periodic Table*
- ▱ **Element or Atom**—How do atoms and elements differ? Elements are substances that are made up of one type of atom, while atoms are the smallest particles of an element that retain the chemical properties of the element. In other words, an element is composed of one or more of the same type of atom. So, when you hold a lump of iron ore, you are holding the element iron, which contains billions of iron atoms.

(Optional) Additional topic to explore this week: *Usborne Science Encyclopedia pp. 24-25 The elements, pp. 28-29 The Periodic Table*

Discussion Questions

After reading the selected pages from the encyclopedias, ask the following questions in your discussion time:

Elements

? What is every element made up of?

? What is the lightest element?

? What is the most reactive metal? Nonmetal?

Periodic Table

? What is the periodic table?

? Who designed the periodic table?

? What is the difference between groups and periods?

(Optional) Additional Books

- *The Elements (True Books)* by Matt Mullins
- *Elements and Compounds (Building Blocks of Matter)* by Louise and Richard Spilsbury
- *The Mystery of the Periodic Table (Living History Library)* by Benjamin D. Wiker, Jeanne Bendick and Theodore Schluenderfritz
- *The Periodic Table (True Books: Elements)* by Salvatore Tocci

Notebooking

Writing Assignments

☐ **Narration Page –** Have the students dictate, copy, or write one to four sentences for elements and the periodic table on SW pg. 20. On the elements image, you will also want the students to label the atomic number, symbol, and atomic mass on the picture. (*See the picture above next to the discussion questions for the answers.*)

☐ **(Optional) Lapbook –** Have the students begin the Periodic Table lapbook by cutting out and coloring the cover on pg. 14.

☐ **(Optional) Lapbook –** Have the students work on the Elements Diagram on pg. 15 of *Chemistry for the Grammar Stage Lapbooking Templates.* Have the students cut out the sheet and label the atomic number, symbol, and atomic mass on the element. Finally, have them glue the sheet into their lapbook.

☐ **(Optional) Lapbook –** Have the students work on the Periodic Table Book on pg. 16 of *Chemistry for the Grammar Stage Lapbooking Templates.* Have the students cut out, fold the template, and color the picture on the cover. Have the students write their narration about the periodic table inside the mini-book. Then glue the mini-book into the lapbook.

Vocabulary

The following definitions are a guide. The students' definitions do not need to match word for word.

- ↻ **Atomic Number** – The number of protons in the nucleus of an atom. (SW pg. 105)
- ↻ **Atomic Mass** – The average mass number of the atoms in a sample of an element. (SW pg. 104)
- ↻ **Element** – A substance made up of one type of atom, which cannot be broken down by chemical reaction to form a simpler substance. (SW pg. 108)
- ↻ **Chemical Symbol** – A shorthand way of representing a specific element in formulae and equations. (SW pg. 106)
- ↻ **Periodic Table** – A systematic arrangement of the elements in order of increasing atomic number. (SW pg. 112)

Multi-week Projects and Activities

Unit Project

- ✂ **Atoms and Molecules Poster** – This week, have the students add an element complete with its atomic number, atomic mass, and symbol to the "atoms and elements" section of their poster. After the students finish the artwork, have them write a sentence or two about elements.

Projects for this Week

- ✂ **Coloring Pages** – You can have the students color the following pages from *Chemistry for the Grammar Stage Coloring Pages*: Periodic Table pg. 12.
- ✂ **Element Report** – Have the students flip through *Basher's Science The Periodic Table* and choose an element to learn more about. Have them read the selected page and then create a poster for the element. The poster should include the basic chemical information for the element (i.e., its atomic number, atomic mass, and symbol), along with where the element is found, several uses for it, and its physical appearance. If you have older students, you can have them do a bit of additional on-line research for this project as well.
- ✂ **Periodic Table Game** – Have the students play a game of Periodic Table Battleship! You can see directions and print out game sheets at the following website:
  - 🖱 http://teachbesideme.com/periodic-table-battleship/

Memorization

🗣 This week, begin working on memorizing the *Periodic Table* poem. (SW pg. 119)

Quiz

Weekly Quiz

- 🗣 "Periodic Table Unit Week 1 Quiz" on SW pg. Q-9.

Quiz Answers

1. See the labeled-element picture under discussion questions.
2. True
3. False (*An element is made up of one single type of atom.*)
4. Answers will vary

Possible Schedules for Week 1

Two Days a Week Schedule	
Day 1	**Day 2**
❏ Read about Elements ❏ Add information about elements and label the atomic number, atomic mass, and chemical symbol on the students' Narration Page ❏ Do the Scientific Demonstration: Table Sorting ❏ Define atomic number, atomic mass, and element	❏ Read about The Periodic Table ❏ Add information about the periodic table to the students' Narration Page ❏ Define chemical symbol and periodic table ❏ Finish the Atoms and Molecules Poster ❏ Work on memorizing the *Periodic Table* poem ❏ Give Periodic Table Week 1 quiz

Five Days a Week Schedule				
Day 1	**Day 2**	**Day 3**	**Day 4**	**Day 5**
❏ Do the Scientific Demonstration: Table Sorting ❏ Define atomic number, atomic mass, and element ❏ Choose one or more of the additional books to read from this week	❏ Read about Elements ❏ Add information about elements and label the atomic number, atomic mass, and chemical symbol on the students' Narration Page	❏ Read one or more of the additional suggested books ❏ Complete the Elements Project ❏ Define chemical symbol and periodic table	❏ Read about The Periodic Table ❏ Add information about the periodic table to the students' Narration Page ❏ Complete the Periodic Table Project	❏ Give Periodic Table Week 1 quiz ❏ Finish the Atoms and Molecules Poster from Unit 1
All Week Long				
❏ Work on memorizing the *Periodic Table* poem				

Week 2: Alkali Metals Lesson Plans

Scientific Demonstration: Colder Water

Supplies Needed
- ✓ Metal can
- ✓ Thermometer
- ✓ Table salt (*Sodium Chloride*)
- ✓ Crushed ice

Purpose
This demonstration is meant to help the students see how the addition of table salt, which contains the alkali metal sodium, can lower the temperature of water.

Instructions and Explanation
The instructions and explanation for this scientific demonstration are found on pp. 122-123 of *Janice VanCleave's Chemistry for Every Kid*. Have the students complete the Lab Report on SW pg. 23.

Take it Further
Have the students look at how table salt changes the rate at which water freezes using the following activity from our website:
- 🖱 http://elementalscience.com/blogs/science-activities/83744963-which-one-freezes-first

Science-Oriented Books

Reading Assignments
- 📖 *Scholastic's The Periodic Table pp. 24-25 Alkali Metals, pp. 20-21 Hydrogen, pp. 28-29 Sodium*
- 📖 *Basher Science The Periodic Table pg. 10 Alkali Metals, pg. 8 Hydrogen, pg. 14 Sodium*

(Optional) Additional topic to explore this week: *Scholastic's The Periodic Table pp. 26-27, Basher Science Periodic Table Lithium, Potassium, Rubidium, Cesium, and Francium*

Discussion Questions
After reading the selected pages from the encyclopedias, ask the following questions in your discussion time:

Alkali Metals
- ❓ What do the alkali metals want to do?
- ❓ What are some of the characteristics of alkali metals?

Hydrogen
- ❓ What are some characteristics of hydrogen?
- ❓ How does hydrogen exist on earth?

Sodium
- ❓ What are some characteristics of sodium?

? Where can you find sodium?

(Optional) Additional Books

- 📖 *The Alkali Metals: Lithium, Sodium, Potassium, Rubidium, Cesium, Francium (Understanding the Elements of the Periodic Table)* by Kristi Lew
- 📖 *Hydrogen and the Noble Gases (True Books: Elements)* by Salvatore Tocci
- 📖 *Hydrogen: Running on Water (Energy Revolution)* by Niki Walker
- 📖 *Sodium (Elements)* by Anne O'Daly
- 📖 *Sodium (True Books: Elements)* by Salvatore Tocci

Notebooking

Writing Assignments

- ☐ **Narration Page** – Have the students dictate, copy, or write one to four sentences about alkali metals, hydrogen, and sodium on SW pg. 22.
- ☐ **(Optional) Lapbook** – Have the students work on the Central Periodic Table on pg. 18 of *Chemistry for the Grammar Stage Lapbooking Templates*. Have the students cut out the periodic table template and glue it into their lapbook. Then, color the alkali metals red.
- ☐ **(Optional) Lapbook** – Have the students work on the Alkali Flip-book on pg. 17 of *Chemistry for the Grammar Stage Lapbooking Templates*. Have the students cut along the solid lines and color the group on the cover red. Next, have the students write several characteristics of alkali metals on the characteristics tab, as well as several facts about hydrogen and sodium on the respective tabs. Then, have them line the pages up and staple the sheets together. Finally, have them glue the flip-book into the lapbook.

Vocabulary

The following definition is a guide. The students' definitions do not need to match word for word.

- ✎ **Reactive** – The tendency of a substance to react with other substances. (SW pg. 114)

Multi-week Projects and Activities

Unit Project

- ✂ **Periodic Table Poster** – Over the next several weeks, the students will make a poster of the periodic table as they learn about the different groups. You can use the blank sheet found in the student workbook on pg. 18 or you can make your own wall-sized periodic table. The pictures for the groups of the periodic table are found in the SW Appendix on pgs. 127 & 129. This week, have the students cut out the alkali metal group, color it red, and add it do the blank table

Projects for this Week

- ✂ **Coloring Pages** – You can have the students color the following pages from *Chemistry for the Grammar Stage Coloring Pages*: Alkali Metals pg. 13.
- ✂ **Alkali Metals** – Have the students eat the alkali metal potassium found in a banana!

Potassium is a key elemental to life. It helps our nerves function properly and aids the brain in transmitting messages to our muscles.

✂ **Hydrogen –** Have the students learn about the *Hindenburg*, which was an air ship filled with hydrogen. You can read the following books with your students:

📖 *You Wouldn't Want to Be on the Hindenburg!* by Ian Graham

📖 *The Hindenburg Disaster (True Books: Disasters)* by Peter Benoit

Please preview these books to make sure that they are appropriate for your students.

✂ **Sodium –** Have the students learn about the chemistry of another sodium compound in your kitchen, baking soda, a.k.a. sodium bicarbonate. Add 1 Tablespoon of baking soda to a cup. Then, have the students add a few drops of white vinegar and observe what happens! (*This is the classic acid (vinegar) and base (baking soda) reaction. The bubbles you see are a release of the energy and the products from the reaction—carbon dioxide gas, sodium acetate, and water.*)

Memorization

● This week, continue to work on memorizing the *Periodic Table* poem. (SW pg. 119)

Quiz

Weekly Quiz

🗡 "Periodic Table Unit Week 2 Quiz" on SW pg. Q-10.

Quiz Answers

1. True
2. Gas
3. Found in lots of common componds; Very reactive; Light grey metal
4. Answers will vary

Possible Schedules for Week 2

| Two Days a Week Schedule ||
Day 1	Day 2
❏ Read about Alkali Metals and Hydrogen ❏ Add information about alkali metals and hydrogen on the students' Narration Page ❏ Add the alkali metals to the Periodic Table Poster ❏ Define reactive	❏ Read about Sodium ❏ Add information about sodium to the students' Narration Page ❏ Do the Scientific Demonstration: Colder Water ❏ Work on memorizing the *Periodic Table* poem ❏ Give Periodic Table Week 2 quiz

| Five Days a Week Schedule |||||
Day 1	Day 2	Day 3	Day 4	Day 5
❏ Read about Alkali Metals ❏ Add information about alkali metals on the students' Narration Page ❏ Complete the Alkali Metals Project	❏ Read about Hydrogen ❏ Add information about hydrogen on the students' Narration Page ❏ Complete the Hydrogen Project	❏ Read about Sodium ❏ Add information about sodium to the students' Narration Page ❏ Complete the Sodium Project	❏ Do the Scientific Demonstration: Colder Water ❏ Define reactive ❏ Choose one or more of the additional books to read from this week	❏ Give Periodic Table Week 2 quiz ❏ Add the alkali metals to the Periodic Table Poster
All Week Long				
❏ Work on memorizing the *Periodic Table* poem				

Week 3: Alkaline Earth Metals Lesson Plans

Scientific Demonstration: Magnesium Milk

Supplies Needed
- ✓ Epsom Salts
- ✓ Ammonia
- ✓ Clear jar

Purpose
This demonstration is meant to help the students create a magnesium compound, which contains an alkaline earth metal.

Instructions and Explanation
The instructions and explanation for this scientific demonstration are found on pp. 100-101 of *Janice VanCleave's Chemistry for Every Kid*. Have the students complete the Lab Report on SW pg. 25.

Take it Further
Make some magnesium crystals with your students. You will need Epsom salts, water, and a small jar. Mix ½ cup of Epsom salts with ½ cup of warm water. Stir to dissolve and place the jar in the refrigerator. Check the jar several hours later and you should see a jar full of crystals!

Science-Oriented Books

Reading Assignments
- 📖 *Scholastic's The Periodic Table pp. 34-35 Alkaline Earth Metals, pg. 37 Magnesium, pp. 40-41 Calcium*
- 📖 *Basher Science The Periodic Table pg. 22 Alkaline Earth Metals, pg. 26 Magnesium, pg. 28 Calcium*

(Optional) Additional topic to explore this week: *Scholastic's The Periodic Table pg. 36 and pp. 44-45, Basher Science Periodic Table Beryllium, Strontium, Barium, and Radium*

Discussion Questions
After reading the selected pages from the encyclopedias, ask the following questions in your discussion time:

Alkaline Earth Metals
- **?** What element do alkaline earth metals like to bond to?
- **?** What are some of the characteristics of alkaline earth metals?

Magnesium
- **?** What are some characteristics of magnesium?
- **?** Where can you find magnesium?

Calcium
? What are some characteristics of calcium?
? Where can you find calcium?

(Optional) Additional Books
- 📖 *The Alkaline Earth Metals: Beryllium, Magnesium, Calcium, Strontium, Barium, Radium (Understanding the Elements of the Periodic Table)* by Bridget Heos
- 📖 *Calcium (True Books: Elements)* by Salvatore Tocci
- 📖 *Magnesium (The Elements)* by Colin Uttley

Notebooking

Writing Assignments
- ☐ **Narration Page** – Have the students dictate, copy, or write one to four sentences about alkaline earth metals, magnesium, and calcium on SW pg. 24.
- ☐ **(Optional) Lapbook** – Have the students work on the Central Periodic Table. This week, have the students color the alkaline earth metals orange.
- ☐ **(Optional) Lapbook** – Have the students work on the Alkaline Earth Flip-book on pg. 19 of *Chemistry for the Grammar Stage Lapbooking Templates*. Have the students cut along the solid lines and color the group on the cover orange. Next, have the students write several characteristics of alkaline earth metals on the characteristics tab as well as several facts about magnesium and calcium on the respective tabs. Then, line the pages up and staple the sheets together. Finally, glue the flip-book into the lapbook.

Vocabulary
- ✐ *There are no vocabulary words for this week.*

Multi-week Projects and Activities

Unit Project
- ✂ **Periodic Table Poster** – This week, have the students cut out the alkaline earth metal group, color it orange, and add it do the blank table in the student workbook on pg. 18 or your wall-sized periodic table. The pictures for the groups of the periodic table are found in the SW Appendix on pgs. 127 & 129.

Projects for this Week
- ✂ **Coloring Pages** – You can have the students color the following pages from *Chemistry for the Grammar Stage Coloring Pages*: Alkaline Earth Metals pg. 14.
- ✂ **Alkaline Earth Metals** – Several of the alkaline earth elements are responsible for giving fireworks their colors. Learn more about the chemistry of fireworks in the following video:
  - 🖰 https://www.youtube.com/watch?v=nPHegSulI_M
- ✂ **Magnesium** – Have the students eat their veggies! Magnesium is one of the elements

that is essential to keep our body working properly. We can get the magnesium we need from green veggies, but unfortunately when you boil veggies too long a lot of the beneficial magnesium compounds come out. However, if you add a pinch of baking soda the magnesium will stay put. This week, boil two batches of the green veggies of your choice: broccoli or spinach are good options. Add a pinch of baking soda to one of the pots and have the students observe the difference.

✂ **Calcium –** Have the students dissolve some calcium! You will need an egg, white vinegar, and a clear glass. Place the egg in the glass and cover it with vinegar. Cover the glass, set it aside, and wait for twenty-four hours. The next day, pour out the vinegar and observe the changes to the shell. (*The shell of the egg contains calcium, which is dissolved by the acid in vinegar.*)

Memorization

📢 This week, continue to work on memorizing the *Periodic Table* poem. (SW pg. 119)

Quiz

Weekly Quiz

⚡ "Periodic Table Unit Week 3 Quiz" on SW pg. Q-11.

Quiz Answers

1. Soft metals; Often bonded to oxygen; React easily
2. False (*Magnesium is a solid metal that burns with a bright white light.*)
3. Students' answers can include the following: bones, teeth, hard water, limestone, cement, and chalk
4. Answers will vary

Possible Schedules for Week 3

Two Days a Week Schedule	
Day 1	**Day 2**
❑ Read about Alkaline Earth Metals and Magnesium ❑ Add information about alkaline earth metals and magnesium on the students' Narration Page ❑ Do the Scientific Demonstration: Magnesium Milk	❑ Read about Calcium ❑ Add information about calcium to the students' Narration Page ❑ Add the alkaline earth metals to the Periodic Table Poster ❑ Work on memorizing the *Periodic Table* poem ❑ Give Periodic Table Week 3 quiz

Five Days a Week Schedule				
Day 1	**Day 2**	**Day 3**	**Day 4**	**Day 5**
❑ Read about Alkaline Earth Metals ❑ Add information about alkaline earth metals on the students' Narration Page ❑ Complete the Alkaline Earth Metals Project	❑ Do the Scientific Demonstration: Magnesium Milk ❑ Choose one or more of the additional books to read from this week	❑ Read about Magnesium ❑ Add information about magnesium on the students' Narration Page ❑ Complete the Magnesium Project	❑ Read about Calcium ❑ Add information about calcium on the students' Narration Page ❑ Complete the Calcium Project	❑ Give Periodic Table Week 3 quiz ❑ Add the alkaline earth metals to the Periodic Table Poster
All Week Long				
❑ Work on memorizing the *Periodic Table* poem				

Week 4: Transition Metals Lesson Plans

Scientific Demonstration: Drinkable Iron

Supplies Needed
- ✓ 3 Tea bags
- ✓ 4 Different types of juice
- ✓ Clear plastic glasses
- ✓ Tablespoon

Purpose
This demonstration is meant to help the students see the presence of iron, a transition metal, in juices.

Instructions and Explanation
The instructions and explanation for this scientific demonstration are found on pp. 112-113 of *Janice VanCleave's Chemistry for Every Kid.* Have the students complete the Lab Report on SW pg. 27.

Take it Further
Have the students test other brands or other drinks you have in your house for the presence of iron.

Science-Oriented Books

Reading Assignments
- 📖 *Scholastic's The Periodic Table pp. 52-53 Transition Metals, pp. 60-61 Iron, pp.70-71 Copper*
- 📖 *Basher Science The Periodic Table pg. 34 Transition Elements, pg. 44 Iron, pg. 48 Copper*

(Optional) Additional topic to explore this week: *Scholastic's The Periodic Table - Any of the remaining Transition Metals from pg. 54 to pg. 101, Basher Science Periodic Table - Any of the remaining Transition Elements*

Discussion Questions
After reading the selected pages from the encyclopedias, ask the following questions in your discussion time:

Transition Metals
- **?** What is the amazing ability of transition metals?
- **?** What are some of the characteristics of transition metals?

Iron
- **?** What are some characteristics of iron?
- **?** Where can you find iron?

Copper
- **?** What are some characteristics of copper?
- **?** Where can you find copper?

(Optional) Additional Books

- *The Transition Elements: The 37 Transition Metals (Understanding the Elements of the Periodic Table)* by Mary-Lane Kamberg
- *Iron (Elements)* by Giles Sparrow
- *Copper (The Elements)* by Richard Beatty

Notebooking

Writing Assignments

- ☐ **Narration Page** – Have the students dictate, copy, or write one to four sentences about transition metals, iron, and copper on SW pg. 26.
- ☐ **(Optional) Lapbook** – Have the students work on the Central Periodic Table. This week, have the students color the transition metals yellow.
- ☐ **(Optional) Lapbook** – Have the students work on the Transition Metals Tab-book on pp. 20-21 of *Chemistry for the Grammar Stage Lapbooking Templates*. Have the students cut along the solid lines and color the group on the cover yellow. Next, have the students write several characteristics of transition metals on the characteristics tab, as well as several facts about iron and copper on the respective tabs. Then, have them line the pages up and staple the sheets together. Finally, glue the tab-book into the lapbook.

Vocabulary

The following definition is a guide. The students' definitions do not need to match word for word.

- ✐ **Metal** – The largest class of elements, usually they are shiny and solid at room temperature. (SW pg. 110)
- ✐ **Alloy** – A mixture of two or more metals or a metal and a non-metal. (SW pg. 104)

Multi-week Projects and Activities

Unit Project

- ✂ **Periodic Table Poster** – This week, have the students cut out the transition metal group, color it yellow, and add it do the blank table in the student workbook on pg. 18 or your wall-sized periodic table. The pictures for the groups of the periodic table are found in the SW Appendix on pgs. 127 & 129.

Projects for this Week

- ✂ **Coloring Pages** – You can have the students color the following pages from *Chemistry for the Grammar Stage Coloring Pages*: Transition Metals pg. 15.
- ✂ **Transition Metals** – Many of the elements in the transitional group are in items we have in our house. Print out a copy of the transition metal hunt sheet from the Appendix on pg. 189. Then, let the students hunt around the house for the metals listed on the sheet and color in any of the elements they find. If you want to make a game out of this, the person with the most elements colored in wins.

✂ **Iron –** Have the students research the uses of iron throughout history and write a one paragraph report or create a poster advertisement with what they find.

✂ **Copper –** Have the students turn copper pennies green. The instructions and explanation for this scientific demonstration are found on pp. 92-93 of *Janice VanCleave's Chemistry for Every Kid*.

Memorization

🗣 This week, continue to work on memorizing the *Periodic Table* poem. (SW pg. 119)

Quiz

Weekly Quiz

🔹 "Periodic Table Unit Week 4 Quiz" on SW pg. Q-12.

Quiz Answers

1. Bond
2. True
3. Pennies
4. Answers will vary

Possible Schedules for Week 4

Two Days a Week Schedule	
Day 1	**Day 2**
❑ Read about Transition Metals and Copper	❑ Read about Iron
❑ Add information about transition metals and copper on the students' Narration Page	❑ Add information about iron to the students' Narration Page
❑ Add the transition metals to the Periodic Table Poster	❑ Do the Scientific Demonstration: Drinkable Iron
❑ Define metal and alloy	❑ Give Periodic Table Week 4 quiz
❑ Work on memorizing the *Periodic Table* poem	

Five Days a Week Schedule				
Day 1	**Day 2**	**Day 3**	**Day 4**	**Day 5**
❑ Read about Transition Metals ❑ Add information about transition metals on the students' Narration Page ❑ Complete the Transition Metals Project	❑ Do the Scientific Demonstration: Drinkable Iron ❑ Choose one or more of the additional books to read from this week ❑ Define metal and alloy	❑ Read about Iron ❑ Add information about iron on the students' Narration Page ❑ Complete the Iron Project	❑ Read about Copper ❑ Add information about copper on the students' Narration Page ❑ Complete the Copper Project	❑ Give Periodic Table Week 4 quiz ❑ Add the transition metals to the Periodic Table Poster
All Week Long				
❑ Work on memorizing the *Periodic Table* poem				

Week 5: Boron Elements Lesson Plans

Scientific Demonstration: Sinking Gel

Supplies Needed
- ✓ Alum powder
- ✓ Ammonia
- ✓ Clear jar

Purpose

This demonstration is meant to help the students create an aluminum compound, which contains a main group metal.

Instructions and Explanation

The instructions and explanation for this scientific demonstration are found on pp. 98-99 of *Janice VanCleave's Chemistry for Every Kid*. Have the students complete the Lab Report on SW pg. 29.

Take it Further

Have the students examine another aluminum-containing compound found in your kitchen, aluminum foil. Have them examine a sheet and note its appearance. If you want to learn about how foil is made, you can watch the following video:

🖱 https://www.youtube.com/watch?v=f4OTj9yNOak

Science-Oriented Books

Reading Assignments

The elements in weeks 5 to 8 can be separated into 4 groups (boron elements, carbon elements, nitrogen elements, and oxygen elements), which are vertical lines on the periodic table, or into 3 families (poor metals, metalloids, and nonmetals), which show the relationships between the characteristics of the elements. For this study, we have chosen to leave them as groups, so if you will notice a few differences in the reading assignments.

- 📖 *Scholastic's The Periodic Table pp. 102-103 Poor Metals, pg. 118 Boron, pp. 104–105 Aluminum*
- 📖 *Basher Science The Periodic Table pg. 76 Boron Elements, pg. 78 Boron, pg. 80 Aluminum*

(Optional) Additional topic to explore this week: *Scholastic's The Periodic Table pp. 106–107, pg. 109, and pg. 114; Basher Science Periodic Table Gallium, Indium, Thallium, Element 113 (Nihonium)*

Discussion Questions

After reading the selected pages from the encyclopedias, ask the following questions in your discussion time:

Boron Elements (Poor Metals)

? (*For Basher Readers Only*) How reactive are boron elements?

? (*For Scholastic's Readers Only*) Which of the boron elements are considered poor metals? Metalloids? (*Refer to the periodic table on Scholastic's The Periodic Table pg. 15 if students need help answering this.*)

? What are some of the characteristics of boron elements?

Boron

? What are some characteristics of boron?

? Where can you find boron?

Aluminum

? What are some characteristics of aluminum?

? Where can you find aluminum?

(Optional) Additional Books

- *The Boron Elements: Boron, Aluminum, Gallium, Indium, Thallium (Understanding the Elements of the Periodic Table)* by Heather Hasan
- *Aluminum* by Heather Hasan
- *Boron (Elements)* by Richard Beatty

Notebooking

Writing Assignments

- ☐ **Narration Page** – Have the students dictate, copy, or write one to four sentences about boron elements, aluminum, and boron on SW pg. 28.
- ☐ **(Optional) Lapbook** – Have the students work on the Central Periodic Table. This week, have the students color the boron elements light green.
- ☐ **(Optional) Lapbook** – Have the students work on the Boron Elements Flip-book on pg. 22 of *Chemistry for the Grammar Stage Lapbooking Templates*. Have the students cut along the solid lines and color the group on the cover light green. Next, have the students write several characteristics of boron elements on the characteristics tab as well as several facts about aluminum and boron on the respective tabs. Then, have them line the pages up and staple the sheets together. Finally, glue the flip-book into the lapbook.

Vocabulary

The following definition is a guide. The students' definitions do not need to match word for word.

- ✎ **Metalloid** – An element that shares some of the properties of metals and nonmetals. (SW pg. 110)

Multi-week Projects and Activities

Unit Project

- ✂ **Periodic Table Poster** – This week, have the students cut out the boron elements group, color it light green, and add it do the blank table in the student workbook on pg. 18 or your wall-sized periodic table. The pictures for the groups of the periodic table are found in the SW Appendix on pgs. 127 & 129.

Projects for this Week

✂ **Coloring Pages** – You can have the students color the following pages from *Chemistry for the Grammar Stage Coloring Pages*: Boron Elements pg. 16.

✂ **Boron Elements** – Have the students learn about indium, which is used to make an electrically-conductive ink. This ink is used in UPC codes, solar cells, and LCD screens. Older students can share what they have learned as a poster or in a paragraph.

✂ **Boron** – Have the students make slime using borax, a boron-containing compound. You will need gel glue, water, and Borax, which can be found in the laundry aisle. In a plastic baggie, have the students mix equal parts of glue and water. Meanwhile, in a cup, mix a quarter cup of water with half a teaspoon of Borax. Then, add the Borax solution to the baggie and have the students massage the bag for a few minutes until a nice firm slime has formed.

✂ **Aluminum** – Have the students watch a neat reaction where aluminum foil gets dissolved. The video can be viewed at the following link:
🖱 https://www.youtube.com/watch?v=AAKdc7PO3J0

Memorization

🗣 This week, continue to work on memorizing the *Periodic Table* poem. (SW pg. 119)

Quiz

Weekly Quiz

🖋 "Periodic Table Unit Week 5 Quiz" on SW pg. Q-13.

Quiz Answers

1. True
2. False (*Boron is the only nonmetal in the group of metallic boron elements.*)
3. An abundant
4. Answers will vary

Possible Schedules for Week 5

Two Days a Week Schedule	
Day 1	Day 2
❑ Read about Boron Elements (or Poor Metals) and Boron ❑ Add information about boron elements and boron on the students' Narration Page ❑ Add the boron elements to the Periodic Table Poster ❑ Define metalloid ❑ Work on memorizing the *Periodic Table* poem	❑ Read about Aluminum ❑ Add information about aluminum to the students' Narration Page ❑ Do the Scientific Demonstration: Sinking Gel ❑ Give Periodic Table Week 5 quiz

Five Days a Week Schedule				
Day 1	Day 2	Day 3	Day 4	Day 5
❑ Read about Boron Elements (or Poor Metals) ❑ Add information about boron elements on the students' Narration Page ❑ Complete the Boron Elements Project	❑ Do the Scientific Demonstration: Sinkable Gel ❑ Choose one or more of the additional books to read from this week ❑ Define metalloid	❑ Read about Aluminum ❑ Add information about aluminum on the students' Narration Page ❑ Complete the Aluminum Project	❑ Read about Boron ❑ Add information about boron on the students' Narration Page ❑ Complete the Boron Project	❑ Give Periodic Table Week 5 quiz ❑ Add the boron elements to the Periodic Table Poster
All Week Long				
❑ Work on memorizing the *Periodic Table* poem				

Week 6: Carbon Elements Lesson Plans

Scientific Demonstration: Chemical Breath

Supplies Needed
- ✓ Limewater (*Note - You will need to make this 24 hours before doing this demonstration. You will need powdered lime, water, and a jar with a lid.*)
- ✓ Straw
- ✓ Cup

Purpose
This demonstration is meant to help the students test for the presence of carbon dioxide, which contains the element carbon, in their breath.

Instructions and Explanation
For this demonstration, you will need to make the limewater the day before. The directions for making the limewater can be found on pp. 70-71 of *Janice VanCleave's Chemistry for Every Kid*. The instructions and explanation for the "Chemical Breath" demonstration are found on pp. 72-73 of *Janice VanCleave's Chemistry for Every Kid*. Have the students complete the Lab Report on SW pg. 31.

Take it Further
Have the students observe how yeast can produce carbon dioxide. The instructions and explanation for this scientific demonstration are found on pp. 74-75 of *Janice VanCleave's Chemistry for Every Kid*.

Science-Oriented Books

Reading Assignments
- 📖 *Scholastic's The Periodic Table pp. 116-117 Metalloids, pp. 162-163 Carbon, pg. 108 Tin*
- 📖 *Basher Science The Periodic Table pg. 86 Carbon Elements, pg. 88 Carbon, pg. 93 Tin*

(Optional) Additional topic to explore this week: *Scholastic's The Periodic Table pg. 119, pg. 122, pp. 110-111, and pg. 114; Basher Science Periodic Table Silicon, Germanium, Lead, Flerovium*

Discussion Questions
After reading the selected pages from the encyclopedias, ask the following questions in your discussion time:

Carbon Elements (Metalloids)
- **?** (*For Basher Readers Only*) How reactive are the carbon elements?
- **?** (*For Scholastic's Readers Only*) Which of the carbon elements are considered metalloids? Poor metals? Nonmetals? (*Refer to the periodic table on Scholastic's The Periodic Table pg. 15 if students need help answering this.*)
- **?** What are some of the characteristics of carbon elements?

Carbon

? What are some characteristics of carbon?

? Where can you find carbon?

? Why is carbon so important to us?

Tin

? What are some characteristics of tin?

? Where can you find tin?

(Optional) Additional Books

- *The Carbon Elements: Carbon, Silicon, Germanium, Tin, Lead (Understanding the Elements of the Periodic Table)* by Brian Belval
- *Carbon* by Linda Saucerman
- *Carbon (True Books: Elements)* by Salvatore Tocci
- *Tin (True Books: Elements)* by Salvatore Tocci
- *The Invention of the Silicon Chip: A Revolution in Daily Life* by Windsor Chorlton

Notebooking

Writing Assignments

- **Narration Page –** Have the students dictate, copy, or write one to four sentences about carbon elements, carbon, and tin on SW pg. 30.
- **(Optional) Lapbook –** Have the students work on the Central Periodic Table. This week, have the students color the carbon elements dark green.
- **(Optional) Lapbook –** Have the students work on the Carbon Elements Flip-book on pg. 23 of *Chemistry for the Grammar Stage Lapbooking Templates*. Have the students cut along the solid lines and color the group on the cover dark green. Next, have the students write several characteristics of carbon elements on the characteristics tab as well as several facts about carbon and tin on the respective tabs. Then, line the pages up and staple the sheets together. Finally, glue the flip-book into the lapbook.

Vocabulary

The following definition is a guide. The students' definitions do not need to match word for word.

Nonmetal – A class of elements that can be non-shiny solids or gases. (SW pg. 112)

Multi-week Projects and Activities

Unit Project

- **Periodic Table Poster –** This week, have the students cut out the carbon elements group, color it dark green, and add it do the blank table in the student workbook on pg. 18 or your wall-sized periodic table. The pictures for the groups of the periodic table are found in the SW Appendix on pgs. 127 & 129.

Projects for this Week

✂ **Coloring Pages** – You can have the students color the following pages from *Chemistry for the Grammar Stage Coloring Pages*: Carbon Elements pg. 17.

✂ **Carbon Elements** – Have the students play with silly putty, which is a silicone polymer with long chains of silicon, oxygen, carbon, and hydrogen.

✂ **Carbon** – Have the students test for the presence of carbon in rocks. Have them choose a rock, such as limestone, place it in a cup, and cover the rock with white vinegar. Have the students observe what happens. (*If there is the presence of bubbles coming from the rock, it is carbonated.*)

✂ **Tin** – Have the students make a tin can luminary. You will need a tin can, a nail, permanent marker, hammer, and a candle. You can find the directions for this project from the following website:

🖱 http://www.thechaosandtheclutter.com/archives/tin-can-luminaries

Memorization

🗣 This week, continue to work on memorizing the *Periodic Table* poem. (SW pg. 119)

Quiz

Weekly Quiz

🎗 "Periodic Table Unit Week 6 Quiz" on SW pg. Q-14.

Quiz Answers

1. Metals, Nonmetals
2. Students' answers will vary, but they should include that carbon is the basis for all life.
3. False (*Tin cans are coated with only a thing layer of tin.*)
4. Answers will vary

Possible Schedules for Week 6

Two Days a Week Schedule	
Day 1	Day 2
❏ Read about Carbon Elements (or Metalloids) and Tin ❏ Add information about carbon elements and tin on the students' Narration Page ❏ Add the carbon elements to the Periodic Table Poster ❏ Define nonmetal ❏ Work on memorizing the *Periodic Table* poem	❏ Read about Carbon ❏ Add information about carbon to the students' Narration Page ❏ Do the Scientific Demonstration: Chemical Breath ❏ Give Periodic Table Week 6 quiz

Five Days a Week Schedule				
Day 1	Day 2	Day 3	Day 4	Day 5
❏ Read about Carbon Elements (or Metalloids) ❏ Add information about carbon elements on the students' Narration Page ❏ Complete the Carbon Elements Project	❏ Do the Scientific Demonstration: Chemical Breath ❏ Choose one or more of the additional books to read from this week ❏ Define nonmetal	❏ Read about Carbon ❏ Add information about carbon on the students' Narration Page ❏ Complete the Carbon Project	❏ Read about Tin ❏ Add information about tin on the students' Narration Page ❏ Complete the Tin Project	❏ Give Periodic Table Week 6 quiz ❏ Add the carbon elements to the Periodic Table Poster
All Week Long				
❏ Work on memorizing the *Periodic Table* poem				

Week 7: Nitrogen Elements Lesson Plans

Scientific Demonstration: Shiny Pennies

Supplies Needed
- ✓ Can of dark cola soda
- ✓ Glass
- ✓ Dirty Pennies

Purpose
This demonstration is meant to help the students to see how phosphoric acid, which contains phosphorus, can help to clean a penny.

Instructions
1. Have the students place several dirty pennies in a cup. Then, pour enough cola into the cup to cover the pennies.
2. Set the cup aside and let it sit undisturbed overnight.
3. The next morning, fish out the pennies and have the students observe the differences. When you are done, pour the cola down the drain. (*Note - Do not drink the cola as it now has copper ions in it!*)

Have the students complete the Lab Report on SW pg. 33.

Explanation
Dark cola has phosphoric acid in it, something that gives the soda its tangy flavor. This acid also breaks up the copper-oxygen compound that, with time, makes pennies dark and dull.

Take it Further
Have the students see if they can get the same results from other kitchen acids, like lemon juice, tea, milk, and other types of soda. (*Note - The students will learn more about acids and bases in Unit 6.*)

Science-Oriented Books

Reading Assignments
- 📖 *Scholastic's The Periodic Table pp. 160-161 Nonmetals, pg. 168-169 Nitrogen, pp.170-171 Phosphorus*
- 📖 *Basher Science The Periodic Table pg. 96 Nitrogen Elements, pg. 98 Nitrogen, pg. 100 Phosphorus*

(Optional) Additional topic to explore this week: *Scholastic's The Periodic Table pp. 124-125, pg. 122, pg. 109, and pg. 114; Basher Science Periodic Table Arsenic, Antimony, Bismuth, Element 115 (Moscovium)*

Discussion Questions
After reading the selected pages from the encyclopedias, ask the following questions in

your discussion time:

Nitrogen Elements (Nonmetals)

? (*For Basher Readers Only*) What type of elements are in this group?

? (*For Scholastic's Readers Only*) Which of the nitrogen elements are considered metalloids? Poor metals? Nonmetals? (*Refer to the periodic table on Scholastic's The Periodic Table pg. 15 if students need help answering this.*)

? What are some of the characteristics of nitrogen elements?

Nitrogen

? What are some characteristics of nitrogen?

? Where can you find nitrogen?

Phosphorus

? What are some characteristics of phosphorus?

? Where can you find phosphorus?

(Optional) Additional Books

- *The Nitrogen Elements (Understanding the Elements of the Periodic Table)* by Greg Roza
- *Nitrogen (True Books: Elements)* by Salvatore Tocci
- *Nitrogen* by Heather Hasan
- *Phosphorus (Elements)* by Richard Beatty

Notebooking

Writing Assignments

☐ **Narration Page –** Have the students dictate, copy, or write one to four sentences about nitrogen elements, nitrogen, and phosphorus on SW pg. 32.

☐ **(Optional) Lapbook –** Have the students work on the Central Periodic Table. This week, have the students color the nitrogen elements light blue.

☐ **(Optional) Lapbook –** Have the students work on the Nitrogen Elements Flip-book on pg. 24 of *Chemistry for the Grammar Stage Lapbooking Templates*. Have the students cut along the solid lines and color the group on the cover light blue. Next, have the students write several characteristics of nitrogen elements on the characteristics tab, as well as several facts about nitrogen and phosphorus on the respective tabs. Then, line the pages up and staple the sheets together. Finally, glue the flip-book into the lapbook.

Vocabulary

The following definition is a guide. The students' definitions do not need to match word for word.

✐ **Essential Element –** An element that is essential to life on earth, such as carbon, hydrogen, nitrogen, and oxygen. (SW pg. 108)

Multi-week Projects and Activities

Unit Project

✂ **Periodic Table Poster –** This week, have the students cut out the nitrogen elements group, color it light blue, and add it do the blank table in the student workbook on pg. 18 or your wall-sized periodic table. The pictures for the groups of the periodic table are found in the SW Appendix on pgs. 127 & 129.

Projects for this Week

✂ **Coloring Pages** – You can have the students color the following pages from *Chemistry for the Grammar Stage Coloring Pages*: Nitrogen Elements pg. 18.

✂ **Nitrogen Elements** – Bismuth, one of the elements in the nitrogen elements group, is often used in makeup and medicine. Have the students head to your bathroom to look for items that contain bismuth. (*Look for things that have a pearly shine, due to bismuth oxychloride, and a certain pink antacid named from the element.*)

✂ **Nitrogen** – Have the students learn more about the nitrogen cycle by watching the following video:
   🖱 https://www.youtube.com/watch?v=ZaFVfHftzpI
   If you would like for your students to also learn about the phosphorus cycle, you can have them watch the following video:
   🖱 https://www.youtube.com/watch?v=wdAzQSuypCk

✂ **Phosphorus** – Have the students learn about the three different types of phosphorus and their uses by reading *Usborne Science Encyclopedia* pg. 55. You can also have older students create a chart with the similarities and differences of the three different types.

Memorization

🗣 This week, continue to work on memorizing the *Periodic Table* poem. (SW pg. 119)

Quiz

Weekly Quiz
   ↳ "Periodic Table Unit Week 7 Quiz" on SW pg. Q-15.

Quiz Answers
   1. True
   2. 80 %
   3. Appears in red, black, and white; Is essential to life; Found in fertilizer
   4. Answers will vary

Possible Schedules for Week 7

Two Days a Week Schedule	
Day 1	**Day 2**
❑ Read about Nitrogen Elements (or Nonmetals) and Nitrogen ❑ Add information about nitrogen elements and nitrogen on the students' Narration Page ❑ Add the nitrogen elements to the Periodic Table Poster ❑ Define essential element ❑ Work on memorizing the *Periodic Table* poem	❑ Read about Phosphorus ❑ Add information about phosphorus to the students' Narration Page ❑ Do the Scientific Demonstration: Shiny Pennies ❑ Give Periodic Table Week 7 quiz

Five Days a Week Schedule				
Day 1	**Day 2**	**Day 3**	**Day 4**	**Day 5**
❑ Read about Nitrogen Elements (or Nonmetals) ❑ Add information about nitrogen elements on the students' Narration Page ❑ Complete the Nitrogen Elements Project	❑ Read about Nitrogen ❑ Add information about nitrogen on the students' Narration Page ❑ Complete the Nitrogen Project	❑ Do the Scientific Demonstration: Shiny Pennies ❑ Choose one or more of the additional books to read from this week ❑ Define essential element	❑ Read about Phosphorus ❑ Add information about phosphorus to the students' Narration Page ❑ Complete the Phosphorus Project	❑ Give Periodic Table Week 7 quiz ❑ Add the nitrogen elements to the Periodic Table Poster
All Week Long				
❑ Work on memorizing the *Periodic Table* poem				

Week 8: Oxygen Elements Lesson Plans

Scientific Demonstration: Browning Apple

Supplies Needed
✓ Apple
✓ Vitamin C tablet

Purpose
This demonstration is meant to help the students see how oxygen can affect and change an apple.

Instructions and Explanation
The instructions and explanation for this scientific demonstration are found on pp. 80-81 of *Janice VanCleave's Chemistry for Every Kid.* Have the students complete the Lab Report on SW pg. 35.

Take it Further
Explain to the students that the process they have just observed is called oxidation. This process is what causes fruit to rot and metal to rust. Then, soak a piece of steel wool in vinegar for about an hour. Take the steel wool out and place it on a paper towel to observe another oxidation reaction. (*You should that the steel wool begins to rust as soon as it hits the air.*)

Science-Oriented Books

Reading Assignments
- *Scholastic's The Periodic Table pp. 158-159 (Life in Color - omit sections on the halogens and noble gases), pp. 174-175 Oxygen, pg. 176 Sulfur*
- *Basher Science The Periodic Table pg. 106 Oxygen Elements, pg. 108 Oxygen, pg. 110 Sulfur*

(Optional) Additional topic to explore this week: *Scholastic's The Periodic Table pg. 177, pg. 123, pg. 109, and pg. 114; Basher Science Periodic Table Selenium, Tellurium, Polonium, Livermorium*

Discussion Questions
After reading the selected pages from the encyclopedias, ask the following questions in your discussion time:

Oxygen Elements (Life in Color)
? (*For Basher Readers Only*) What type of elements are in this group?
? (*For Scholastic's Readers Only*) Which of the oxygen elements are considered metalloids? Poor metals? Nonmetals? (*Refer to the periodic table on Scholastic's The Periodic Table pg. 15 if students need help answering this.*)
? What are some of the characteristics of oxygen elements?

Oxygen
? What are some characteristics of oxygen?

? Where can you find oxygen?

Sulfur

? What are some characteristics of sulfur?

? Where can you find sulfur?

(Optional) Additional Books

- 📖 *The Oxygen Elements: Oxygen, Sulfur, Selenium, Tellurium, Polonium (Understanding the Elements of the Periodic Table)* by Laura La Bella
- 📖 *Nonmetals (Material Matters/Freestyle Express)* by Carol Baldwin
- 📖 *Oxygen (True Books: Elements)* by Salvatore Tocci
- 📖 *Sulfur (The Elements)* by Richard Beatty

Notebooking

Writing Assignments

- ☐ **Narration Page** – Have the students dictate, copy, or write one to four sentences about oxygen elements, oxygen, and sulfur on SW pg. 34.
- ☐ **(Optional) Lapbook** – Have the students work on the Central Periodic Table. This week, have the students color the oxygen elements dark blue.
- ☐ **(Optional) Lapbook** – Have the students work on the Oxygen Elements Flip-book on pg. 25 of *Chemistry for the Grammar Stage Lapbooking Templates*. Have the students cut along the solid lines and color the group on the cover dark blue. Next, have the students write several characteristics of oxygen elements on the characteristics tab, as well as several facts about oxygen and sulfur on the respective tabs. Then, line the pages up and staple the sheets together. Finally, glue the flip-book into the lapbook.

Vocabulary

The following definition is a guide. The students' definitions do not need to match word for word.

- ✐ **Oxidation** – A chemical reaction in which a substance combines with oxygen. (SW pg. 112)

Multi-week Projects and Activities

Unit Project

- ✂ **Periodic Table Poster** – This week have the students cut out the oxygen elements group, color it dark blue, and add it do the blank table in the student workbook on pg. 18 or your wall-sized periodic table. The pictures for the groups of the periodic table are found in the SW Appendix on pgs. 127 & 129.

Projects for this Week

- ✂ **Coloring Pages** – You can have the students color the following pages from *Chemistry for the Grammar Stage Coloring Pages*: Oxygen Elements pg. 19.

✂ **Oxygen Elements –** Have the students research a bit about selenium and its uses. Selenium is one of the most abundant oxygen elements on earth after oxygen. Older students can share what they have learned as a poster or in a paragraph.

✂ **Oxygen –** Have the students watch the following video about oxygen:
  ☝ http://easyscienceforkids.com/oxygen-element-video-for-kids/

✂ **Sulfur –** Have the students experience the smell of sulfur! You will need a vegetable with a high sulfur content, such as cabbage, brussel sprouts, or turnips. Cut the vegetable in half, smell both halves, and set one half aside. Then, cut the remaining half in half again and boil the two quarters. After 10 minutes remove one of the quarters and have the students compare the smells between the cooked and uncooked portions. Wait 10 more minutes and then remove the remaining quarter from the boiling water. Have the students compare the smells of all three slices. (*The students should note an increasing "rotten-eggs" smell in the cooked portions of the vegetable. The heat causes the bonds to break, which releases the stinky sulfur-containing compound, hydrogen sulfide.*)

Memorization

● This week, continue to work on memorizing the *Periodic Table* poem. (SW pg. 119)

Quiz

Weekly Quiz
  ⚘ "Periodic Table Unit Week 8 Quiz" on SW pg. Q-16.

Quiz Answers
  1. Important
  2. Students' answers will vary, but they should include that oxygen is fuel for our body or that it is the powerhouse behind most chemical reactions on Earth.
  3. True
  4. Answers will vary

Possible Schedules for Week 8

Two Days a Week Schedule	
Day 1	Day 2
❑ Read about Oxygen Elements (or Life in Color) and Sulfur ❑ Add information about oxygen elements and sulfur on the students' Narration Page ❑ Add the oxygen elements to the Periodic Table Poster ❑ Define oxidation ❑ Work on memorizing the *Periodic Table* poem	❑ Read about Oxygen ❑ Add information about oxygen to the students' Narration Page ❑ Do the Scientific Demonstration: Browning Apples ❑ Give Periodic Table Week 8 quiz

Five Days a Week Schedule				
Day 1	Day 2	Day 3	Day 4	Day 5
❑ Read about Oxygen Elements (or Life in Color) ❑ Add information about oxygen elements on the students' Narration Page ❑ Complete the Oxygen Elements Project	❑ Do the Scientific Demonstration: Browning Apples ❑ Choose one or more of the additional books to read from this week ❑ Define oxidation	❑ Read about Oxygen ❑ Add information about oxygen to the students' Narration Page ❑ Complete the Oxygen Project	❑ Read about Sulfur ❑ Add information about sulfur to the students' Narration Page ❑ Complete the Sulfur Project	❑ Give Periodic Table Week 8 quiz ❑ Add the oxygen elements to the Periodic Table Poster
All Week Long				
❑ Work on memorizing the *Periodic Table* poem				

Week 9: Halogens Lesson Plans

Scientific Demonstration: Magic Writing

Supplies Needed
- ✓ Iodine swab
- ✓ Notebook paper
- ✓ Lemon juice
- ✓ Cup
- ✓ Paint brush

Purpose
This demonstration is meant to help the students see how iodine, a halogen element, can help to reveal a secret message!

Instructions and Explanation
The instructions and explanation for this scientific demonstration are found on pp. 80-81 of *Janice VanCleave's Chemistry for Every Kid*. Have the students complete the Lab Report on SW pg. 37. (*Note – To make this demonstration a bit easier to do, we recommend using an iodine swab rather than making your own iodine solution as suggested in the book.*)

Take it Further
Try another method for revealing secret messages with your students. You can follow the directions in this post:

🖱 http://elementalblogging.com/science-corner-sending-a-secret-message/

Science-Oriented Books

Reading Assignments
- 📖 *Scholastic's The Periodic Table pp. 182–183 Halogens, pg. 184 Fluorine, pg. 189 Iodine*
- 📖 *Basher Science The Periodic Table pg. 116 Halogens, pg. 118 Fluorine, pg. 124 Iodine*

(Optional) Additional topic to explore this week: *Scholastic's The Periodic Table pg. 185 and pg. 188; Basher Science Periodic Table Chlorine, Bromine, Astatine, Element 117*

Discussion Questions
After reading the selected pages from the encyclopedias, ask the following questions in your discussion time:

Halogens
- **?** What type of elements are in this group?
- **?** What are some of the characteristics of halogens?

Fluorine
- **?** What are some characteristics of fluorine?
- **?** Where can you find fluorine?

Iodine
? What are some characteristics of iodine?

? Where can you find iodine?

(Optional) Additional Books
- 📖 *Fluorine (Understanding the Elements of the Periodic Table)* by Heather Hasan
- 📖 *The Elements: Iodine* by Leon Gray
- 📖 *Iodine (Understanding the Elements of the Periodic Table)* by Kristi Lew

Notebooking

Writing Assignments
- ☐ **Narration Page –** Have the students dictate, copy, or write one to four sentences about halogens, fluorine, and iodine on SW pg. 36.
- ☐ **(Optional) Lapbook –** Have the students work on the Central Periodic Table. This week, have the students color the halogens purple.
- ☐ **(Optional) Lapbook –** Have the students work on the Halogens Flip-book on pg. 26 of *Chemistry for the Grammar Stage Lapbooking Templates*. Have the students cut along the solid lines and color the group on the cover purple. Next, have the students write several characteristics of halogens on the characteristics tab, as well as several facts about fluorine and iodine on the respective tabs. Then, have them line the pages up and staple the sheets together. Finally, glue the flip-book into the lapbook.

Vocabulary
The following definition is a guide. The students' definitions do not need to match word for word.
- 🖋 **Ion –** An atom or group of atoms that has become charged by gaining or losing one or more electrons. (SW pg. 110)

Multi-week Projects and Activities

Unit Project
- ✂ **Periodic Table Poster –** This week, have the students cut out the halogens group, color it purple, and add it do the blank table in the student workbook on pg. 18 or your wall-sized periodic table. The pictures for the groups of the periodic table are found in the SW Appendix on pgs. 127 & 129.

Projects for this Week
- ✂ **Coloring Pages –** You can have the students color the following pages from *Chemistry for the Grammar Stage Coloring Pages*: Halogens pg. 20.
- ✂ **Halogens –** Have the students watch the following video showing the different reactivities of the halogens:
  - 🖱 https://www.youtube.com/watch?v=saLvwX3_p1s
- ✂ **Fluorine –** Fluorine is often used in toothpaste to help protect the enamel on teeth from

being dissolved. Have the students test this ability using an egg. You will need two eggs, fluoride toothpaste, plastic wrap, white vinegar, and an egg. Coat one of the eggs with the toothpaste, wrap it in plastic wrap, and set it in the fridge overnight. After 24 hours, gently rinse off any excess toothpaste with warm water and mark it with an "F" using a permanent maker. Then, set both eggs in a cup, cover them with vinegar, and watch what happens. (*The students should see that the egg marked with an "F" does not dissolve nearly as quickly as the one without.*)

✂ **Iodine –** Have the students use the iodine swab from the demonstration to test different foods in your kitchen for the presence of starch. (*Iodine is brown-black normally, but will change to blue-purple in the presence of a starch.*)

Memorization

This week, continue to work on memorizing the *Periodic Table* poem. (SW pg. 119)

Quiz

Weekly Quiz

"Periodic Table Unit Week 9 Quiz" on SW pg. Q-17.

Quiz Answers

1. False (*The elements in the halogens group are very reactive.*)
2. Drinking water; Teflon coatings
3. True
4. Answers will vary

Possible Schedules for Week 9

Two Days a Week Schedule	
Day 1	Day 2
❑ Read about Halogens and Fluorine	❑ Read about Iodine
❑ Add information about oxygen elements and sulfur on the students' Narration Page	❑ Add information about iodine to the students' Narration Page
❑ Add the oxygen elements to the Periodic Table Poster	❑ Do the Scientific Demonstration: Magic Writing
❑ Define ion	❑ Give Periodic Table Week 9 quiz
❑ Work on memorizing the *Periodic Table* poem	

Five Days a Week Schedule				
Day 1	Day 2	Day 3	Day 4	Day 5
❑ Read about Halogens ❑ Add information about halogens on the students' Narration Page ❑ Complete the Halogens Project	❑ Read about Fluorine ❑ Add information about fluorine to the students' Narration Page ❑ Complete the Fluorine Project	❑ Do the Scientific Demonstration: Magic Writing ❑ Choose one or more of the additional books to read from this week ❑ Define ion	❑ Read about Iodine ❑ Add information about iodine to the students' Narration Page ❑ Complete the Iodine Project	❑ Give Periodic Table Week 9 quiz ❑ Add the halogens to the Periodic Table Poster
All Week Long ❑ Work on memorizing the *Periodic Table* poem				

Week 10: Noble Gas Lesson Plans

Scientific Demonstration: Funny Voice

Supplies Needed
- ✓ Helium-filled balloon
- ✓ Scissors

Purpose
This demonstration is meant to let the students see how helium can change the sound of your voice.

Instructions
(*CAUTION - Helium is non-toxic, but it can cause light-headedness. Do NOT let the students do this activity - you need to demonstrate it for them. Do NOT repeat it more than once and be sure to follow the directions.*)

1. Pinch the base of a helium-filled balloon just under the knot and cut off the end so that you can get some of the gas to release.
2. Exhale completely and place the cut balloon just under your chin.
3. As you inhale, open the balloon so that you breathe in some of the helium. Then, start to talk or sing so that the students can observe the difference in your voice.
4. Have the students complete the Lab Report on SW pg. 39.

Explanation
Your students should observe that your voice now has a squeaky quality to it and may even seem to be a bit higher. This is because Helium is six times lighter than air, so the sound waves of your voice speed up as they pass through the gas, causing your voice to sound squeaky.

Take it Further
There is no "Take it Further" activity for this week.

Science-Oriented Books

Reading Assignments
- 📖 *Scholastic's The Periodic Table pp. 190-191 Noble Gases, pg. 192 Helium, pg. 193 Neon*
- 📖 *Basher Science The Periodic Table pg. 128 Noble Gases, pg. 130 Helium, pg. 132 Neon*

(Optional) Additional topic to explore this week: *Scholastic's The Periodic Table pp. 194-195; Basher Science Periodic Table Argon, Krypton, Xenon, Radon, Element 118*

Discussion Questions
After reading the selected pages from the encyclopedias, ask the following questions in your discussion time:

Noble Gases
? What type of elements are in this group?

? What are some of the characteristics of noble gases?

Helium

? What are some characteristics of helium?

? Where can you find helium?

Neon

? What are some characteristics of neon?

? Where can you find neon?

(Optional) Additional Books

- *Hydrogen and the Noble Gases (True Books: Elements) by Salvatore Tocci*
- *Krypton (Understanding the Elements of the Periodic Table) by Janey Levy*

Notebooking

Writing Assignments

- **Narration Page –** Have the students dictate, copy, or write one to four sentences about noble gases, helium, and neon on SW pg. 38.
- **(Optional) Lapbook –** Have the students work on the Central Periodic Table. This week, have the students color the noble gases gray.
- **(Optional) Lapbook –** Have the students work on the Noble Gases Flip-book on pg. 27 of *Chemistry for the Grammar Stage Lapbooking Templates*. Have the students cut along the solid lines and color the group on the cover gray. Next, have the students write several characteristics of noble gases on the characteristics tab as well as several facts about helium and neon on the respective tabs. Then, line the pages up and staple the sheets together. Finally, glue the flip-book into the lapbook.

Vocabulary

The following definition is a guide. The students' definitions do not need to match word for word.

- **Inert –** An element that is completely nonreactive. (SW pg. 109)

Multi-week Projects and Activities

Unit Project

- **Periodic Table Poster –** This week have the students cut out the noble gases group, color it gray, and add it do the blank table in the student workbook on pg. 18 or your wall-sized periodic table. The pictures for the groups of the periodic table are found in the SW Appendix on pgs. 127 & 129.

Projects for this Week

- **Coloring Pages –** You can have the students color the following pages from *Chemistry for the Grammar Stage Coloring Pages*: Noble Gases pg. 21.
- **Noble Gases –** Radon is a noble gas that is one of the products of radioactive decay. It can build up in the basements of homes that sit over natural deposits of thorium or

uranium. If there is radon present in a house, contractors can install a system that flushes it out. See if you live in radon zone:

⊖ http://www.epa.gov/radon/epa-map-radon-zones

✂ **Helium –** Have the students learn more about the history of helium-filled blimps by watching the following video:

⊖ https://www.youtube.com/watch?v=vfpv6JXMaGM

✂ **Neon –** Head out on field trip to look for neon lights! You may want to read the following article beforehand so that you understand how neon lights work and what elements give them their color:

⊖ http://www.ehow.com/how-does_4927221_neon-its-colors.html

Memorization

🗣 This week, continue to work on memorizing the *Periodic Table* poem. (SW pg. 119)

Quiz

Weekly Quiz

⚷ "Periodic Table Unit Week 10 Quiz" on SW pg. Q-18.

Quiz Answers

1. Least
2. False (*Helium is lighter than air.*)
3. Excited
4. Answers will vary

Possible Schedules for Week 10

Two Days a Week Schedule	
Day 1	**Day 2**
❏ Read about Noble Gases and Neon	❏ Read about Helium
❏ Add information about noble gases and neon on the students' Narration Page	❏ Add information about helium to the students' Narration Page
❏ Add the noble gases to the Periodic Table Poster	❏ Do the Scientific Demonstration: Funny Voice
❏ Define inert	❏ Give Periodic Table Week 10 quiz
❏ Work on memorizing the *Periodic Table* poem	

Five Days a Week Schedule				
Day 1	**Day 2**	**Day 3**	**Day 4**	**Day 5**
❏ Read about Noble Gases ❏ Add information about noble gases on the students' Narration Page ❏ Complete the Noble Gases Project	❏ Do the Scientific Demonstration: Funny Voice ❏ Choose one or more of the additional books to read from this week ❏ Define inert	❏ Read about Helium ❏ Add information about helium to the students' Narration Page ❏ Complete the Helium Project	❏ Read about Neon ❏ Add information about neon on the students' Narration Page ❏ Complete the Neon Project	❏ Give Periodic Table Week 10 quiz ❏ Add the noble gases to the Periodic Table Poster
All Week Long				
❏ Work on memorizing the *Periodic Table* poem				

Week 11: Lanthanides Lesson Plans

Scientific Demonstration: Moving Pencils

Supplies Needed
- ✓ 3 Cups
- ✓ 3 Pencils
- ✓ 3 Clear liquids (i.e., water, alcohol, and corn syrup)

Purpose
This demonstration is meant to help the students understand the concept of refraction.

Instructions
1. Fill each of the three cups halfway with one of the clear liquids.
2. Have the students place a pencil in each of the cups.
3. Then, have them observe what has happened to the pencils.
4. Have the students complete the Lab Report on SW pg. 41.

Explanation
The students should have seen that the pencils appeared to shift or move in the different liquids. This is due to refraction, or the bending of light. One of the Lanthanide elements, Lanthanum, is often used in quality glass lenses so that the image we see is closer to the original one..

Take it Further
Have the students repeat the demonstration with other clear liquids, such as baby oil.

Science-Oriented Books

Reading Assignments
Note – Lathanoids is another name for Lanthanides.
- 📖 *Scholastic's The Periodic Table pg. 128–129 Lanthanoids, pg. 130 Lanthanus, pg. 131 Neodymium*
- 📖 *Basher Science The Periodic Table pg. 140 Lanthanides, pg. 142 Lanthanum, pg. 146 Neodymium*

(Optional) Additional topic to explore this week: *Scholastic's The Periodic Table pp. 132-138; Basher Science Periodic Table - Any of the remaining Lanthanide Elements*

Discussion Questions
After reading the selected pages from the encyclopedias, ask the following questions in your discussion time:

Lanthanides
- **?** What type of elements are in this group?
- **?** What are some of the characteristics of lanthanoid elements?

Lanthanum
? What are some characteristics of lanthanum?
? Where can you find lanthanum?

Neodymium
? What are some characteristics of neodymium?
? Where can you find neodymium?

(Optional) Additional Books
📖 *The Lanthanides (Elements) by Richard Beatty*

Notebooking

Writing Assignments
- **Narration Page** – Have the students dictate, copy, or write one to four sentences about lanthanides, lanthanum, and neodymium on SW pg. 40.
- **(Optional) Lapbook** – Have the students work on the Central Periodic Table. This week, have the students color the brown.
- **(Optional) Lapbook** – Have the students work on the Lanthanides Flip-book on pg. 28 of *Chemistry for the Grammar Stage Lapbooking Templates*. Have the students cut along the solid lines and color the group on the cover brown. Next, have the students write several characteristics of lanthanides on the characteristics tabs, as well as several facts about lanthanum and neodymium on the respective tabs. Then, line the pages up and staple the sheets together. Finally, glue the flip-book into the lapbook.

Vocabulary
The following definition is a guide. The students' definitions do not need to match word for word.
- **Refraction** – The bending of light as it passes through a different medium. (SW pg. 114)

Multi-week Projects and Activities

Unit Project
✂ **Periodic Table Poster** – This week, have the students cut out the lanthanides group, color it brown, and add it do the blank table in the student workbook on pg. 18 or your wall-sized periodic table. The pictures for the groups of the periodic table are found in the SW Appendix on pgs. 127 & 129.

Projects for this Week
✂ **Coloring Pages** – You can have the students color the following pages from *Chemistry for the Grammar Stage Coloring Pages*: Lanthanides pg. 22.

✂ **Lanthanides** – Have the students excite some electrons to make a bulb glow without plugging it in. You will need a woolen mitten or glove and a fluorescent bulb. Head into a dark room, rub the bulb with the woolen mitten, and watch what happens! (*Elements* *like Terbium, a lanthanide that is sometimes used to coat fluorescent bulbs, glow when they are hit by a beam of electrons. When you rub the bulb, you create static electricity, which is basically excited electrons!)*

✂ **Lanthanum –** Have the students play with a prism, which refracts, or bends, the different wavelengths of light at different angles to create a rainbow.

✂ **Neodymium –** Have the students play with neodymium magnets! Be careful to supervise them well with this activity as neodymium magnets are very strong and very dangerous if swallowed.

Memorization

This week, continue to work on memorizing the *Periodic Table* poem. (SW pg. 119)

Quiz

Weekly Quiz

"Periodic Table Unit Week 11 Quiz" onSW pg. Q-19.

Quiz Answers

1. True
2. Good lens
3. Very
4. Answers will vary

Possible Schedules for Week 11

Two Days a Week Schedule	
Day 1	**Day 2**
❑ Read about Lanthanum	❑ Read about Lanthanides and Neodymium
❑ Add information about lanthanum to the students' Narration Page	❑ Add information about lanthanides and neodymium on the students' Narration Page
❑ Do the Scientific Demonstration: Moving Pencils	❑ Add the lanthanides to the Periodic Table Poster
❑ Define refraction	❑ Give Periodic Table Week 11 quiz
❑ Work on memorizing the *Periodic Table* poem	

Five Days a Week Schedule				
Day 1	**Day 2**	**Day 3**	**Day 4**	**Day 5**
❑ Read about Lanthanides ❑ Add information about lanthanides on the students' Narration Page ❑ Complete the Lanthanides Project	❑ Read about Lanthanum ❑ Add information about lanthanum to the students' Narration Page ❑ Complete the Lanthanum Project	❑ Do the Scientific Demonstration: Moving Pencils ❑ Choose one or more of the additional books to read from this week ❑ Define refraction	❑ Read about Neodymium ❑ Add information about neodymium to the students' Narration Page ❑ Complete the Neodymium Project	❑ Give Periodic Table Week 11 quiz ❑ Add the lanthanides to the Periodic Table Poster
All Week Long				
❑ Work on memorizing the *Periodic Table* poem				

Week 12: Actinides Lesson Plans

Scientific Demonstration: Half-life

Supplies Needed
- ✓ Bite-sized food, such as raisins or cereal puffs
- ✓ Timer

Purpose
This demonstration is meant to help the students understand what a half-life is.

Instructions
1. Give the students 32 pieces of the bite-sized food.
2. After 2 minutes, have them eat 16 pieces.
3. After 2 more minutes, have them eat 8 pieces.
4. After 2 more minutes, have them eat 4 pieces.
5. After 2 more minutes, have them eat 2 pieces.
6. After 2 more minutes, have them eat 1 piece.
7. After 2 more minutes, have them break the 1 piece in half and eat one of the halves.
8. After 2 more minutes, have the students eat any of the remaining crumbs.
9. Have the students complete the Lab Report on SW pg. 43.

Explanation
This demonstration was meant to give a students a mental picture of how a half-life works. Many of the actinide elements are radioactive, which means that they are unstable so the elements decay with a half life. The half-life period depends upon the element and how radioactive it is.

Take it Further
There is no "Take it Further" activity for this week.

Science-Oriented Books

Reading Assignments
Note – Actinoids is another name for Actinides.
- 📖 *Scholastic's The Periodic Table pp. 140-141 Actinoids, pp. 144-145 Uranium, pg. 154 Americium*
- 📖 *Basher Science The Periodic Table pg. 158 Actinides, pg. 163 Uranium, pg. 167 Americium*

(Optional) Additional topic to explore this week: *Scholastic's The Periodic Table pp. 142-143, pp. 150-153, and pg. 155; Basher Science Periodic Table – Any of the remaining Actinide Elements*

Discussion Questions
After reading the selected pages from the encyclopedias, ask the following questions in your discussion time:

Actinides
- **?** What type of elements are in this group?
- **?** What are some of the characteristics of actinoid elements?

Uranium
- **?** What are some characteristics of uranium?
- **?** Where can you find uranium?

Americium
- **?** What are some characteristics of americium?
- **?** Where can you find americium?

(Optional) Additional Books
- *Radioactive Elements* by Tom Jackson
- *The 15 Lanthanides and the 15 Actinides (Understanding the Elements of the Periodic Table)* by Kristi Lew

Notebooking

Writing Assignments
- ☐ **Narration Page** – Have the students dictate, copy, or write one to four sentences about actinides, uranium, and americium on SW pg. 42.
- ☐ **(Optional) Lapbook** – Have the students work on the Central Periodic Table. This week, have the students color the actinides white.
- ☐ **(Optional) Lapbook** – Have the students work on the Actinides Flip-book on pg. 29 of *Chemistry for the Grammar Stage Lapbooking Templates*. Have the students cut along the solid lines and color the group on the cover white. Next, have the students write several characteristics of actinides on the characteristics tabs, as well as several facts about uranium and americium on the respective tab. Then, line the pages up and staple the sheets together. Finally, glue the flip-book into the lapbook.
- ☐ **(Optional) Lapbook** – Have the students finish their lapbook. Have them cut out and color the poem on pg. 30 of *Chemistry for the Grammar Stage Lapbooking Templates*. Once they are done, have them glue the sheet into their lapbook.

Vocabulary
The following definition is a guide. The students' definitions do not need to match word for word.
- ✏ **Radioactive Decay** – The process by which a nucleus ejects particles through radiation becoming the nucleus of a series of different elements until stability is reached. (SW pg. 114)

Multi-week Projects and Activities

Unit Project
- ✂ **Periodic Table Poster** – This week, have the students cut out the actinides group, color

it white, and add it do the blank table in the student workbook on pg. 18 or your wall-sized periodic table. The pictures for the groups of the periodic table are found in the SW Appendix on pgs. 127 & 129.

Projects for this Week

- ✂ **Coloring Pages** – You can have the students color the following pages from *Chemistry for the Grammar Stage Coloring Pages*: Actinides pg. 23.
- ✂ **Review** – Have the students review what they have learned so far about the periodic table.
- ✂ **Uranium** – Have the students learn more about nuclear power by watching the following video:

  👆 https://www.youtube.com/watch?v=d7LO8lL4Ai4

  Note—*This video does touch on the dangers of nuclear power vs. other power methods. Please preview this video to make sure it is appropriate for your child.*
- ✂ **Americium** – Have the students learn about how smoke detectors, which contain americium, work. You will need a working smoke detector, a hair dryer, and a bottle of baby powder. Have the students turn the hair dryer on high, aim it at the smoke detector, count to five, and then turn the dryer off. (*The students should see that the heat from the dryer did not set off the alarm.*) Then, hold the detector above the bottle of baby power and squeeze the bottle gently to create a few puffs of baby powder. (*This time the students should see that the smoke detector went off. This is because the americium in the smoke detector charges the nearby air and when new molecules float through this zone, it changes the charge and causes the alarm to sound.*)

Memorization

🗣 This week, continue to work on memorizing the *Periodic Table* poem. (SW pg. 119)

Quiz

Weekly Quiz

🖊 "Periodic Table Unit Week 12 Quiz" on SW pg. Q-20.

Quiz Answers

1. True
2. Stable
3. Generating power
4. Answers will vary

Possible Schedules for Week 12

Two Days a Week Schedule	
Day 1	**Day 2**
❑ Read about Actinides	❑ Read about Uranium and Americium
❑ Add information about actinides to the students' Narration Page	❑ Add information about uranium and americium on the students' Narration Page
❑ Do the Scientific Demonstration: Half-life	❑ Add the actinides to the Periodic Table Poster
❑ Define radioactive decay	❑ Give Periodic Table Week 12 quiz
❑ Work on memorizing the *Periodic Table* poem	

Five Days a Week Schedule				
Day 1	**Day 2**	**Day 3**	**Day 4**	**Day 5**
❑ Read about Actinides ❑ Add information about actinides to the students' Narration Page ❑ Complete the Review Project	❑ Do the Scientific Demonstration: Half-life ❑ Choose one or more of the additional books to read from this week ❑ Define radioactive decay	❑ Read about Uranium ❑ Add information about uranium to the students' Narration Page ❑ Complete the Uranium Project	❑ Read about Americium ❑ Add information about americium to the students' Narration Page ❑ Complete the Americium Project	❑ Give Periodic Table Week 12 quiz ❑ Add the actinides to the Periodic Table Poster

All Week Long

❑ Work on memorizing the *Periodic Table* poem

Periodic Table

1																	2
H Hydrogen 1.008																	**He** Helium 4
3 **Li** Lithium 6.041	4 **Be** Beryllium 9.012											5 **B** Boron 10.81	6 **C** Carbon 12.01	7 **N** Nitrogen 14.01	8 **O** Oxygen 16	9 **F** Fluorine 19	10 **Ne** Neon 20.18
11 **Na** Sodium 22.99	12 **Mg** Magnesium 24.3											13 **Al** Aluminum 26.98	14 **Si** Silicon 28.09	15 **P** Phosphorus 30.97	16 **S** Sulfur 32.07	17 **Cl** Chlorine 35.45	18 **Ar** Argon 39.95
19 **K** Potassium 39.1	20 **Ca** Calcium 40.08	21 **Sc** Scandium 44.96	22 **Ti** Titanium 47.87	23 **V** Vanadium 50.94	24 **Cr** Chromium 52	25 **Mn** Manganese 54.94	26 **Fe** Iron 55.85	27 **Co** Cobalt 58.93	28 **Ni** Nickel 58.69	29 **Cu** Copper 63.55	30 **Zn** Zinc 65.39	31 **Ga** Gallium 69.72	32 **Ge** Germanium 72.61	33 **As** Arsenic 74.92	34 **Se** Selenium 78.96	35 **Br** Bromine 79.9	36 **Kr** Krypton 83.8
37 **Rb** Rubidium 85.47	38 **Sr** Strontium 87.62	39 **Y** Yttrium 88.91	40 **Zr** Zirconium 91.22	41 **Nb** Niobium 92.91	42 **Mo** Molybdenum 95.94	43 **Tc** Technetium 98.91	44 **Ru** Ruthenium 101.07	45 **Rh** Rhodium 102.91	46 **Pd** Palladium 106.42	47 **Ag** Silver 107.87	48 **Cd** Cadmium 112.41	49 **In** Indium 114.82	50 **Sn** Tin 118.71	51 **Sb** Antimony 121.76	52 **Te** Tellurium 127.6	53 **I** Iodine 126.9	54 **Xe** Xenon 131.29
55 **Cs** Cesium 132.9	56 **Ba** Barium 137.3	* 71 **Lu** Lutetium 175	72 **Hf** Hafnium 178.49	73 **Ta** Tantalum 180.95	74 **W** Tungsten 183.85	75 **Re** Rhenium 186.21	76 **Os** Osmium 190.2	77 **Ir** Iridium 192.2	78 **Pt** Platinum 195.08	79 **Au** Gold 196.97	80 **Hg** Mercury 200.59	81 **Tl** Thallium 204.38	82 **Pb** Lead 207.2	83 **Bi** Bismuth 208.98	84 **Po** Polonium 208.98	85 **At** Astatine 209.9	86 **Rn** Radon 222.02
87 **Fr** Francium 223	88 **Ra** Radium 226	** 103 **Lr** Lawrencium 262	104 **Rf** Rutherfordium 261.11	105 **Db** Dubnium 262.11	106 **Sg** Seaborgium 263.12	107 **Bh** Bohrium 264.1	108 **Hs** Hassium 265.1	109 **Mt** Meitnerium 266	110 **Ds** Darmstadtium [271]	111 **Rg** Roentgenium [272]	112 **Cn** Copernicium [277]	113 **Nh** Nihonium	114 **Fl** Flerovium	115 **Mc** Moscovium	116 **Lv** Livermorium	117 **Ts** Tennessine	118 **Og** Oganesson

*Lanthanides

57 **La** Lanthanum 138.91	58 **Ce** Cerium 140.12	59 **Pr** Praseodymium 14.91	60 **Nd** Neodymium 144.24	61 **Pm** Promethium 144.91	62 **Sm** Samarium 150.36	63 **Eu** Europium 151.96	64 **Gd** Gadolinium 157.25	65 **Tb** Terbium 158.93	66 **Dy** Dysprosium 162.5	67 **Ho** Holmium 164.93	68 **Er** Erbium 167.26	69 **Tm** Thulium 168.93	70 **Yb** Ytterbium 173.04

**Actinides

89 **Ac** Actinium 227.03	90 **Th** Thorium 232.04	91 **Pa** Protactinium 231.04	92 **U** Uranium 238.03	93 **Np** Neptunium 237.04	94 **Pu** Plutonium 244.06	95 **Am** Americium 243.06	96 **Cm** Curium 247.07	97 **Bk** Berkelium 247.07	98 **Cf** Californium 251.08	99 **Es** Einsteinium 252.08	100 **Fm** Fermium 257.1	101 **Md** Mendelevium 258.1	102 **No** Nobelium 259.1

Chemistry for the Grammar Stage

Physical Changes Unit

Physical Changes Unit Overview
(4 weeks)

Books Scheduled

Encyclopedias
📖 *Basher Science Chemistry*
OR
📖 *Usborne Science Encyclopedia*

Scientific Demonstrations Book
📖 *JVC Chemistry for Every Kid*

Sequence for Study
↻ **Week 1:** States of Matter
↻ **Week 2:** Changes in State
↻ **Week 3:** Liquid Behavior
↻ **Week 4:** Gas Behavior

Physical Changes Poem to Memorize

<u>States of Matter</u>
Three states of matter
Solid, liquid, gas
Molecules scatter
As heat enters mass

A solid is firm
Atoms locked in tight
No room found to squirm
We can take a bite

Liquid moves freely
Atoms flow and gush
Filling easily
Even helps you flush

A gas has no shape
Moves without control
It tries to escape
Out every hole

Supplies Needed for the Unit

Week	Supplies needed
1	3 Balloons, Ice, Water
2	Orange Juice, Cup
3	3 Toothpicks, Dish soap, Bowl, Water
4	2-Liter soda bottle, Quarter, Water

Unit Vocabulary

1. **States of Matter** – The different forms in which a substance can exist: solid, liquid, and gas.
2. **Volume** – The space occupied by matter.
3. **Physical Change** – A change that occurs in which no new substances are made.
4. **Sublimation** – A change from solid to gas without going through liquid form.
5. **Surface Tension** – A force that pulls together molecules on the surface of a liquid.
6. **Evaporation** – The process by which the surface molecules of a liquid escape into a vapor.
7. **Diffusion** – The spreading out of a gas to fill the available space.

Week 1: States of Matter Lesson Plans

Scientific Demonstration: Playing with Matter

Supplies Needed
- ✓ 3 Balloons
- ✓ Water
- ✓ Ice

Purpose
This demonstration is meant to help the students feel the differences between the three states of matter.

Instructions
1. Fill one balloon with ice, one balloon with water, and one with gas (air).
2. Let the students explore each of the balloons and observe the differences. As they make their observations, ask them questions like:
   - **?** Which one floats the best?
   - **?** Which one is easiest to control?
   - **?** Which one has the most interesting shape?
3. Have the students complete the Lab Report on SW pg. 49.

Explanation
The students should see that the three states of matter have very different physical properties.

Science-Oriented Books

Reading Assignments
- 📖 *Basher Science Chemistry pg. 8 Solid, pg. 10 Liquid, pg. 12 Gas*
- 📖 *Usborne Science Encyclopedia pp. 16–17 Solids, Liquids, and Gases*

Note - *There is also a fourth state of matter, plasma, which is a bit more abstract. It consists of atoms that have been split by high heat or electricity. Since it is difficult for students to be able to visualize plasma, we have left this information out for their first look at the different states of matter.*

(Optional) Additional topics to explore this week: *No additional topics scheduled.*

Discussion Questions
After reading the selected pages, ask the following questions for your discussion time.

Solid
- **?** How much energy does this state of matter have?
- **?** What type of volume and shape do solids have?

Liquid
- **?** How much energy does this state of matter have?
- **?** What type of volume and shape do liquids have?

Gas

? How much energy does this state of matter have?

? What type of volume and shape do gases have?

(Optional) Additional Books

- 📖 *What Is the World Made Of? All About Solids, Liquids, and Gases (Let's-Read-and-Find... Science, Stage 2)* by Kathleen Weidner Zoehfeld and Paul Meisel
- 📖 *Solids, Liquids, And Gases (Rookie Read-About Science)* by Ginger Garrett
- 📖 *States of Matter: A Question and Answer Book* by Bayrock, Fiona, McMullen and Anne

Notebooking

Writing Assignments

- ☐ **Narration Page –** Have the students dictate, copy, or write one to four sentences on solids, liquids, and gases on SW pg. 48.
- ☐ **(Optional) Lapbook –** Have the students begin the Physical and Chemical Changes lapbook by cutting out and coloring the cover on pg. 32.
- ☐ **(Optional) Lapbook –** Have the students complete the States of Matter Cut-flap Book on pg. 33 of *Chemistry for the Grammar Stage Lapbooking Templates.* Have them cut out and fold the template. Have the students color the pictures on the cover. Then, have the students write the definition for solid, liquid, and gas on the inside. Finally, glue the flap-book into the lapbook.

Vocabulary

The following definitions are a guide. The students' definitions do not need to match word for word.

- 🏷 **States of Matter –** The different forms in which a substance can exist: solid, liquid, and gas. (SW pg. 115)
- 🏷 **Volume –** The space occupied by matter. (SW pg. 116)

Multi-week Projects and Activities

Unit Project

- ✂ **Physical Changes Poster –** Over this unit, the students will create a poster depicting the physical changes that substances can go through. This week, have the students divide the poster into three sections. Place solids on the left, liquids in the center, and gases on the right. (*This has been done for you in the SW on pg. 58.*)

Projects for this Week

- ✂ **Coloring Pages –** Have the students color the following pages from *Chemistry for the Grammar Stage Coloring Pages*: Solids pg. 24, Liquids pg. 25, Gases pg. 26.
- ✂ **Solids –** Make a States of Matter float with your students! You will need ice cream, root beer (or other type of soda), and a glass. Have the students add the solid, ice cream, first. Then, pour over the liquid, root beer, and watch the gas bubbles appear!

✂ **Liquids –** Have the students observe with liquids, a.k.a. water play. Provide a bucket and several different sizes of cups for the students to pour and fill. Then, let them loose!

✂ **Gases –** Have the students make a poster depicting how the molecules behave in different states of matter. You will need a pencil, paint, and a sheet of paper. Divide a sheet into three parts and label the sections with solid, liquid, and gas. Then, draw a glass or beaker shape in each section. Have the students use the eraser end of the pencil to dip into the paint and then stamp molecules right next to each other in tightly-packed rows within the solid's beaker. Next, have the students stamp molecules slightly apart from each other within the liquid's beaker. Finally, have the students stamp molecules way apart from each other and even a few escaping from the gas's beaker.

Memorization

🗣 This week, begin working on memorizing the *States of Matter* poem. (SW pg. 120)

Quiz

Weekly Quiz

✦ "Physical Changes Unit Week 1 Quiz" on SW pg. Q-21.

Quiz Answers

1. B, C, A
2. True
3. False (*The molecules in a gas have more energy than the molecules in a solid.*)
4. Answers will vary

Possible Schedules for Week 1

Two Days a Week Schedule	
Day 1	**Day 2**
❑ Do the Scientific Demonstration: Playing with Matter ❑ Define states of matter and volume ❑ Work on memorizing the *States of Matter* poem	❑ Read about Solids, Liquids, and Gases (Solids, Liquids, Gases) ❑ Add information about solids, liquids, and gases to the students' Narration Page ❑ Work on the States of Matter Poster ❑ Give the Physical Changes Week 1 quiz

Five Days a Week Schedule				
Day 1	**Day 2**	**Day 3**	**Day 4**	**Day 5**
❑ Do the Scientific Demonstration: Playing with Matter ❑ Define states of matter and volume ❑ Choose one or more of the additional books to read from this week	❑ Read about Solids, Liquids, and Gases - intro on pg. 16 and density on pg. 17 (Solids) ❑ Add information about solids to the students' Narration Page ❑ Complete the Solids Project	❑ Read about Solids, Liquids, and Gases - volume on pg. 17 (Liquids) ❑ Add information about liquids to the students' Narration Page ❑ Complete the Liquids Project	❑ Read about Solids, Liquids, and Gases - kinetic theory and Brownian motion (Gases) ❑ Add information about gases to the students' Narration Page ❑ Complete the Gases Project	❑ Give the Physical Changes Week 1 quiz ❑ Work on the States of Matter Poster
All Week Long				
❑ Work on memorizing the *States of Matter* poem				

Week 2: Changes in State Lesson Plans

Scientific Demonstration: Freezy Meltdown

Supplies Needed
- ✓ Orange Juice (*Or other juice that your students like to drink.*)
- ✓ Cup

Purpose
This demonstration is meant to help the students see that freezing and melting are both physical changes.

Instructions
1. Pour a bit of juice in a cup for each of the students and have them take a sip of the juice.
2. Have the students place the remaining juice in the freezer.
3. After it has hardened (about an hour or two), take the cup out and have the students observe the changes that have occurred.
4. Let the cup sit on the counter in a place where it won't be disturbed.
5. After the juice has melted (about an hour or two), have the students take a sip of the juice to see if it tastes the same as it did during step 1.
6. Have the students complete the Lab Report on SW pg. 51.

Explanation
The students should see that the juice tastes the same at the beginning as it did at the end. They should have also seen that the juice became solid and did not pour after time in the freezer, and that it became a liquid again after it sat out on the counter. These changes were physical changes, which means that although the physical properties of the juice (liquid or solid) changed, the chemical make-up (the taste) did not. Changes in state, going from a liquid to a solid and vice versa, are known as physical changes.

Take it Further
Have the students repeat the process using different types of liquids to see if the results vary.

Science-Oriented Books

Reading Assignments
- 📖 *Basher Science Chemistry pg. 14, Melting Point, pg. 15 Boiling Point (Note – If you choose this resource, you will need to discuss freezing and condensing with your students.)*
- 📖 *Usborne Science Encyclopedia pp. 18-19 Changes in States*

(Optional) Additional topics to explore this week: *No additional topics scheduled.*

Discussion Questions
After reading the selected pages, ask the following questions for your discussion time.

Changes in State
? What happens when a solid melts (melting point)?

? What happens when a liquid boils (boiling point)?

? What happens when a gas condenses?

? What happens when a liquid freezes?

(Optional) Additional Books

- 📖 *How Water Changes (Weekly Reader: Science)* by Jim Mezzanotte
- 📖 *Solids (States of Matter)* by Jim Mezzanotte
- 📖 *Liquids (States of Matter)* by Jim Mezzanotte
- 📖 *Gases (States of Matter)* Jim Mezzanotte

Notebooking

Writing Assignments

- 🗋 **Narration Page –** Have the students dictate, copy, or write one to two sentences on melting, boiling, freezing, and condensing on SW pg. 50.
- 🗋 **(Optional) Lapbook –** Have the students complete the Changes in State Arrow-book on pg. 34 of *Chemistry for the Grammar Stage Lapbooking Templates.* Have the students cut out and fold the template. Have them color the picture on the cover. Then, have the students write several sentences about what they have learned. Finally, glue the flap-book into the lapbook.

Vocabulary

The following definitions are a guide. The students' definitions do not need to match word for word.

- ✎ **Physical Change –** A change that occurs in which no new substances are made. (SW pg. 113)
- ✎ **Sublimation –** A change from solid to gas without going through liquid form. (SW pg. 115)

Multi-week Projects and Activities

Unit Project

- ✄ **Physical Changes Poster –** This week, have the students add the arrows for the physical changes they have learned about (melting, boiling, freezing, and condensing). Also, have them add pictures of solids or draw examples of solids under the "Solid" category.

Projects for this Week

- ✄ **Coloring Pages –** Have the students color the following pages from *Chemistry for the Grammar Stage Coloring Pages*: Changes in State pg. 27.
- ✄ **Changes in State –** Have the students set several ice cubes on a plate and set the plate out in the hot sun. Check the plate every five minutes to observe what happens. The students should see the solid water (ice) melts into liquid water, which then evaporates into a gas and disappears into the air.

Memorization

🗣 This week, begin working on memorizing the *States of Matter* poem. (SW pg. 120)

Quiz

Weekly Quiz

🔖 "Physical Changes Unit Week 2 Quiz" on SW pg. Q-22.

Quiz Answers

1. Melts, Boils
2. Freezes, Condenses
3. Answers will vary

Possible Schedules for Week 2

Two Days a Week Schedule	
Day 1	**Day 2**
❑ Do the Scientific Demonstration: Freezy Meltdown ❑ Define physical changes and sublimation ❑ Work on memorizing the *States of Matter* poem	❑ Read about Changes in State (Melting point, Boiling point) ❑ Add information about the changes in state to the students' Narration Page ❑ Work on the States of Matter Poster ❑ Give the Physical Changes Week 2 quiz

Five Days a Week Schedule				
Day 1	**Day 2**	**Day 3**	**Day 4**	**Day 5**
❑ Do the Scientific Demonstration: Freezy Meltdown ❑ Define physical changes and sublimation ❑ Choose one or more of the additional books to read from this week	❑ Read about Changes in State - intro on pg. 18 (Melting Point) ❑ Add information about changes in state to the students' Narration Page	❑ Read about Changes in State - intro on pg. 19 (Boiling Point) ❑ Add information about changes in state to the students' Narration Page	❑ Read one or more of the additional books ❑ Complete the Changes in State Project	❑ Give the Physical Changes Week 2 quiz ❑ Work on the States of Matter Poster
All Week Long				
❑ Work on memorizing the *States of Matter* poem				

Week 3: Liquid Behavior Lesson Plans

Scientific Demonstration: Floating Sticks

Supplies Needed
- ✓ 3 Toothpicks
- ✓ Dish soap
- ✓ Bowl
- ✓ Water

Purpose
This demonstration is meant to help the students see what surface tension in water looks like.

Instructions and Explanation
The instructions and explanation for this scientific demonstration are found on pp. 38-39 of *Janice VanCleave's Chemistry for Every Kid.* Have the students complete the Lab Report on SW pg. 53.

Take it Further
Have the students see how water can pull food coloring against gravity. The instructions and explanation for this scientific demonstration are found on pp. 36-37 of *Janice VanCleave's Chemistry for Every Kid.*

Science-Oriented Books

Reading Assignments
- 📖 *Basher Science Chemistry pg. 10 Liquid (There are no new pages in this resource for this week. If you do not wish to re-read the section on liquids, you will need to choose one of the additional books from your library or read from the Usborne Science Encyclopedia for this week.)*
- 📖 *Usborne Science Encyclopedia pp. 20-21 How Liquids Behave*

(Optional) Additional topics to explore this week: *No additional topics scheduled.*

Discussion Questions
After reading the selected pages, ask the following questions for your discussion time.

How Liquids Behave
- **?** Can a liquid change shape?
- **?** Can a liquid change volume?

Evaporation
- **?** What happens as a liquid heats up?
- **?** What affects the rate of evaporation of a liquid?

Surface Tension
- **?** What is surface tension?
- **?** What is cohesion? Adhesion?

(Optional) Additional Books

- 📖 *What Is a Liquid?* (First Step Nonfiction, States of Matter) by Jennifer Boothroyd
- 📖 *How Do You Measure Liquids?* (A+ Books: Measure It!) by Thomas K. Adamson
- 📖 *Saving Water: The Water Cycle* (Do It Yourself) by Buffy Silverman
- 📖 *Why Do Puddles Disappear?: Noticing Forms of Water* by Martha E. H. Rustad and Christine M. Schneider

Notebooking

Writing Assignments

- ☐ **Narration Page** – Have the students dictate, copy, or write one to four sentences on how liquids behave, evaporation, and surface tension on SW pg. 52.
- ☐ **(Optional) Lapbook** – Have the students begin the How States Behave Tab-book on pg. 35 of *Chemistry for the Grammar Stage Lapbooking Templates*. Have them cut out the pages. Have the students color the pictures on the cover. This week, have them write their narration on the liquid tab. They can include information on how liquids behave, evaporation, and surface tension. Then, set the pages aside for next week.

Vocabulary

The following definitions are a guide. The students' definitions do not need to match word for word.

- ✐ **Evaporation** – The process by which the surface molecules of a liquid escape into a vapor. (SW pg. 108)
- ✐ **Surface Tension** – A force that pulls together molecules on the surface of a liquid. (SW pg. 116)

Multi-week Projects and Activities

Unit Project

- ✂ **Physical Changes Poster** – This week, have the students add pictures of liquids or draw examples of liquids under the "Liquid" category.

Projects for this Week

- ✂ **Coloring Pages** – Have the students color the following pages from *Chemistry for the Grammar Stage Coloring Pages*: Evaporation pg. 28, Surface Tension pg. 29.
- ✂ **Liquid Behavior** – Complete the activity suggested on pg. 21 of the *Usborne Science Encyclopedia*.
- ✂ **Evaporation** – Mix together a quarter cup of warm water and a tablespoon of salt. Pour the mixture into a shallow dish and set the dish out in a sunny place. Check the dish every hour or so to observe what happens.
- ✂ **Surface Tension** – Experiment with the surface tension of water. You will need a shallow bowl, liquid soap, and paper clip. Fill the bowl with a thin layer of water and gentle set the paper clip on the top of the water, so that it floats. (*The paper clip is being*

held up by the surface tension of the water.) Then, add a drop of the liquid soap near the paper clip and watch what happens. (*The soap will break the surface tension of the water and the paper clip will fall to the bottom of the bowl.*)

Memorization

This week, continue working on memorizing the *States of Matter* poem. (SW pg. 120)

Quiz

Weekly Quiz

"Physical Changes Unit Week 3 Quiz" on SW pg. Q-23.

Quiz Answers

1. Shape, Volume
2. False (*The hotter a liquid gets, the quicker it evaporates.*)
3. True
4. Answers will vary

Possible Schedules for Week 3

Two Days a Week Schedule	
Day 1	**Day 2**
❑ Do the Scientific Demonstration: Floating Sticks ❑ Define evaporation and surface tension ❑ Work on memorizing the *States of Matter* poem	❑ Read about How Liquids Behave (Liquids) ❑ Add information about the changes in state to the students' Narration Page ❑ Work on the States of Matter Poster ❑ Give the Physical Changes Week 3 quiz

Five Days a Week Schedule				
Day 1	**Day 2**	**Day 3**	**Day 4**	**Day 5**
❑ Do the Scientific Demonstration: Floating Sticks ❑ Define evaporation and surface tension ❑ Choose one or more of the additional books to read from this week	❑ Read about How Liquids Behave - intro on pg. 20 (Liquids) ❑ Add information about how liquids behave to the students' Narration Page ❑ Complete the Liquid Behavior Project	❑ Read about How Liquids Behave - section on evaporation on pg. 20 ❑ Add information about evaporation to the students' Narration Page ❑ Complete the Evaporation Project	❑ Read about How Liquids Behave - sections on pg. 21 ❑ Add information about surface tension to the students' Narration Page ❑ Complete the Surface Tension Project	❑ Give the Physical Changes Week 3 quiz ❑ Work on the States of Matter Poster
All Week Long				
❑ Work on memorizing the *States of Matter* poem				

Week 4: Gas Behavior Lesson Plans

Scientific Demonstration: Clicking Coin

Supplies Needed
- ✓ 2-Liter soda bottle
- ✓ Quarter
- ✓ Water

Purpose
This demonstration is meant to help the students see the effects of expanding gas.

Instructions and Explanation
The instructions and explanation for this scientific demonstration are found on pp. 180-181 of *Janice VanCleave's Chemistry for Every Kid*. Have the students complete the Lab Report on SW pg. 55.

Take it Further
Blow up a balloon and have the students measure the diameter. Then, place the balloon in the freezer for thirty minutes. Take the balloon out and have the students measure the diameter once more. Did it change? (*The students should see that the diameter of the balloon shrank, as matter generally contracts as it cools.*)

Science-Oriented Books

Reading Assignments
- 📖 *Basher Science Chemistry pg. 12 Gas, pg. 14 Brownian Motion*
- 📖 *Usborne Science Encyclopedia pg. 16 Section on Brownian Motion, pp. 22-23 How Gases Behave*

(Optional) Additional topics to explore this week: *No additional topics scheduled.*

Discussion Questions
After reading the selected pages, ask the following questions for your discussion time.

Brownian Motion
? What is Brownian motion?

Diffusion
? What happens in diffusion?
? Where do molecules want to move?

Pressure and Temperature
? What is pressure?
? What happens when you heat a substance up?

(Optional) Additional Books
- 📖 *What Is a Gas? (First Step Nonfiction)* by Jennifer Boothroyd
- 📖 *It's a Gas!* by Ruth Griffin, Margaret Griffin and Pat Cupples

▱ *The Atmosphere: Planetary Heat Engine (Earth's Spheres)*

Notebooking

Writing Assignments
- ☐ **Narration Page –** Have the students dictate, copy, or write one to four sentences on Brownian motion, diffusion, and pressure and temperature on SW pg. 54.
- ☐ **(Optional) Lapbook –** Have the students complete the How States Behave tab-book. This week, have them write their narration on the gases tab. They can include information on Brownian motion, diffusion, and pressure/temperature. Then, staple the pages together and glue the mini-book into the lapbook.

Vocabulary
The following definition is a guide. The students' definitions do not need to match word for word.

✎ **Diffusion –** The spreading out of a gas to fill the available space. (SW pg. 107)

Multi-week Projects and Activities

Unit Project
✂ **Physical Changes Poster –** This week, have the students add pictures of gases or draw examples of gases under the "Gas" category.

Projects for this Week
✂ **Coloring Pages –** Have the students color the following pages from *Chemistry for the Grammar Stage Coloring Pages*: Diffusion pg. 30.

✂ **Brownian Motion –** Have the students create a Brownian motion painting. You will need a small ball (marble or rubber bouncy ball), paint, paper, and a tray. Place the paper in the tray. Then, have the students dip the ball into the paint and place it in the tray. Have them pick up the tray and shake it gently with random motions. The ball will move around and create random paths similar to the Brownian motion of a molecule in a liquid or gas.

✂ **Diffusion –** Have the students use their noses to detect the diffusion of gases. You will need vanilla extract, an eyedropper, and a cotton ball. Place a few drops of vanilla extract on the cotton ball and then wait for a few minutes. Have the students raise their hands as soon as they can smell the vanilla. (*The students are able to smell the vanilla as the molecules of vanilla gas move, or diffuse, through the air to reach their noses.*)

Memorization
🗣 This week, continue working on memorizing the *States of Matter* poem. (SW pg. 120)

Quiz

Weekly Quiz
- "Physical Changes Unit Week 4 Quiz" on SW pg. Q-24.

Quiz Answers
1. True
2. High, Low
3. Pressure
4. Answers will vary

Possible Schedules for Week 4

Two Days a Week Schedule	
Day 1	**Day 2**
❑ Do the Scientific Demonstration: Clicking Coin ❑ Read about How Gases Behave - Diffusion section on pg. 22 (Gas) ❑ Add information about diffusion to the students' Narration Page ❑ Define diffusion ❑ Work on the States of Matter Poster	❑ Read about Brownian Motion and How Gases Behave - pg. 23 (Brownian Motion) ❑ Add information about the Brownian motion and pressure and temperature to the students' Narration Page ❑ Work on memorizing the *States of Matter* poem ❑ Give the Physical Changes Week 4 quiz

Five Days a Week Schedule				
Day 1	**Day 2**	**Day 3**	**Day 4**	**Day 5**
❑ Do the Scientific Demonstration: Clicking Coin ❑ Define diffusion ❑ Choose one or more of the additional books to read from this week	❑ Read about Brownian Motion (Brownian Motion) ❑ Add information about the Brownian motion to the students' Narration Page ❑ Complete the Brownian Motion Project	❑ Read about How Gases Behave - Diffusion section on pg. 22 (Gas) ❑ Add information about diffusion to the students' Narration Page ❑ Complete the Diffusion Project	❑ Read about How Gases Behave - pg. 23 ❑ Add information about pressure and temperature to the students' Narration Page ❑ Read one or more of the additional books	❑ Give the Physical Changes Week 4 quiz ❑ Work on the States of Matter Poster
All Week Long				
❑ Work on memorizing the *States of Matter* poem				

Chemistry for the Grammar Stage

Chemical Changes Unit

Chemical Changes Unit Overview
(4 weeks)

Books Scheduled
Encyclopedias
- *Basher Science Chemistry*
  OR
- *Usborne Science Encyclopedia*

Scientific Demonstrations Book
- *JVC Chemistry for Every Kid*

Sequence for Study
- Week 1: Bonding
- Week 2: Chemical Reactions
- Week 3: Types of Reactions
- Week 4: Oxidation and Reduction

Chemical Changes Poem to Memorize

Reactions
Atoms bump into each other in space
Bonding - connecting at a rapid pace
These compounds form in three main types of bonds
Different ways electrons correspond
In an ionic bond, one atom asks
The other gives electrons to the task
In a covalent bond the atoms share
Electrons joined in a happy pair
The metallic bond is a little strange
Electrons swirl in a constant exchange
This bonding happens in a reaction
Reactants to products - one cool action
As this tidy chemical change occurs
The mass stays the same, it only transfers
Exothermic reactions give off heat
Endothermic ones cool as atoms meet
Catalysts help by speeding up the pace
Redox is when electrons swap their place

Supplies Needed for the Unit

Week	Supplies needed
1	Wax paper, Toothpicks, Eyedroppers, Water
2	Saucer, Paper towel, Vinegar, Pennies
3	Bread, Iodine, Eyedropper, Wax paper
4	Apple, Lemon juice

Unit Vocabulary

1. **Chemical Bond** – A force that holds together two or more atoms.
2. **Chemical Reaction** – An occurrence where the atoms in substances are rearranged to form new substances.
3. **Catalyst** – A substance that speeds up a chemical reaction.
4. **Enzyme** – A catalyst that speeds up a chemical reaction in living things.
5. **Redox Reaction** – A chemical reaction that involves the transfer of electrons.

Week 1: Bonding Lesson Plans

Scientific Demonstration: Moving Drop

Supplies Needed
- ✓ Wax paper
- ✓ Toothpicks
- ✓ Eyedroppers
- ✓ Water

Purpose
This demonstration is meant to help the students see the attractive force of water molecules.

Instructions and Explanation
The instructions and explanation for this scientific demonstration are found on pp. 50-51 of *Janice VanCleave's Chemistry for Every Kid*. Have the students complete the Lab Report on SW pg. 61.

Take it Further
Have the students see the power of the attractive force of surface molecules of water. The instructions and explanation for this scientific demonstration are found on pp. 48-49 of *Janice VanCleave's Chemistry for Every Kid*.

Science-Oriented Books

Reading Assignments
- 📖 *Basher Science Chemistry pg. 30 Ions, pg. 34 Giant molecules, pg. 36 Metallic bonding* (**Note** – *If you choose to use only this resource with your students, you will need to also read the definitions for ionic and covalent bonding from the glossary.*)
- 📖 *Usborne Science Encyclopedia pp. 68–70 Bonding*

(Optional) Additional topics to explore this week: *Basher Chemistry pg.32 (Molecules), Usborne pg. 71 (sections on valency and allotropes)*

Discussion Questions
After reading the selected pages, ask the following questions for your discussion time.

Ionic bonding
- **?** What is an ion?
- **?** How is an ionic bond formed?
- **?** What types of elements form an ionic bond?

Covalent bonding
- **?** How is a covalent bond formed?
- **?** What types of elements form a covalent bond?
- **?** What is a giant molecule?

Metallic bonding
? How is a metallic bond formed?

? What types of elements form a metallic bond?

(Optional) Additional Books
There are no additional books on the market for these topics. Instead, you can watch the following videos on bonding:

- Covalent bonding - https://www.youtube.com/watch?v=LkAykOv1foc
- Ionic bonding - https://www.youtube.com/watch?v=DEdRcfyYnSQ
- Chemical bonding - https://www.youtube.com/watch?v=_M9khs87xQ8

Notebooking

Writing Assignments
- ☐ **Narration Page** – Have the students dictate, copy, or write one to four sentences on covalent bonding, ionic bonding, and metallic bonding on SW pg. 60.
- ☐ **(Optional) Lapbook** – Have the students complete the Bonding Triangle-book on pg. 36 of *Chemistry for the Grammar Stage Lapbooking Templates*. Have them cut out and fold the templates. Have the students color the cover and glue it on the outside. Then, have the students write the definition for covalent, ionic, and metallic bonding on the inside. Finally, glue the triangle-book into the lapbook.

Vocabulary
The following definition is a guide. The students' definitions do not need to match word for word.

- **Chemical Bond** – A force that holds together two or more atoms. (SW pg. 105)

Multi-week Projects and Activities

Unit Project
- ✂ **Chemical Changes Poster** – Over the course of this unit, the students will create a poster about depicting the three types of bonding and the different chemical reactions. This week, have them divide the top half of their posters into three sections labeled - covalent, ionic, and metallic. Under each section the students can include how the type of bond is formed, what types of elements form that particular bond, and examples of substances that have that type of bonding. (*This has been done for you in the SW on pg. 58.*)

Projects for this Week
- ✂ **Coloring Pages** – Have the students color the following pages from *Chemistry for the Grammar Stage Coloring Pages*: Bonding pg. 31.
- ✂ **Bonding Art** – Have the students learn about bonding by creating an artistic representation of the different types of bonds. You will need two colors of paint, paper, a few pom-pom balls, and a pencil eraser. Here are the directions:
  - **Ionic bonding** – Have the students dip a pom-pom in one color of paint and use it

to make nine dots in two circles, two in a center circle and seven in a surrounding circle, leaving space for one more in the outer circle. Now take another pom-pom and dip in the other color of paint to make a dot in the space left in the outer circle you previously made, creating an artistic ionic bond.

- **Covalent bonding** – Have the students dip a pom-pom into one of the colors of paint and use it to make ten dots in two circles, two in a center circle and eight in a surrounding circle. Then, have them cut a pom-pom in half and dip it into the other color of paint. Use the half pom-pom to paint over half of the two of the dots in the outer circle they made previously, creating an artistic covalent bond.
- **Metallic bonding** – Have the students dip a pom-pom into one of the colors of paint and then make a 4 by 3 grid on the paper. (*Be sure to leave space in the grid for the mini-dots.*) Then, have them dip the end of the pencil eraser into the other color of paint and use it to randomly scatter the mini-dots in between grid they made previously, creating an artistic metallic bond.

Memorization

This week, begin working on memorizing the *Reactions* poem. (SW pg. 121)

Quiz

Weekly Quiz

"Chemical Changes Unit Week 1 Quiz" on SW pg. Q-25.

Quiz Answers

1. Ionic
2. Metallic
3. Covalent
4. Answers will vary

Possible Schedules for Week 1

Two Days a Week Schedule	
Day 1	**Day 2**
❑ Read about Bonding - pg. 68 and ionic bonding section on pg. 70 (Ions) ❑ Add information about ionic bonding to the students' Narration Page ❑ Do the Scientific Demonstration: Moving Drop ❑ Define chemical bond	❑ Read about Bonding - pg. 69 and metallic bonding section on pg. 70 (Giant molecules, Metallic bonding) ❑ Add information about covalent and metallic bonding to the students' Narration Page ❑ Work on memorizing the *Reactions* poem ❑ Work on the Chemical Changes Poster ❑ Give the Chemical Changes Week 1 quiz

Five Days a Week Schedule				
Day 1	**Day 2**	**Day 3**	**Day 4**	**Day 5**
❑ Do the Scientific Demonstration: Moving Drop ❑ Define chemical bond ❑ Choose one or more of the additional books to read from this week	❑ Read about Bonding - pg. 68 and ionic bonding section on pg. 70 (Ions) ❑ Add information about ionic bonding to the students' Narration Page ❑ Complete the Ionic Bonding Art Project	❑ Read about Bonding - pg. 69 (Giant molecules) ❑ Add information about covalent bonding to the students' Narration Page ❑ Complete the Covalent Bonding Art Project	❑ Read about Bonding – metallic bonding section on pg. 70 (Metallic bonding) ❑ Add information about metallic bonding to the students' Narration Page ❑ Complete the Metallic Bonding Art Project	❑ Give the Chemical Changes Week 1 quiz ❑ Work on the Chemical Changes Poster
All Week Long				
❑ Work on memorizing the *Reactions* poem				

Week 2: Chemical Reactions Lesson Plans

Scientific Demonstration: Green Pennies

Supplies Needed
- ✓ Saucer
- ✓ Paper towel
- ✓ Vinegar
- ✓ Pennies

Purpose
This demonstration is meant to help the students see a chemical change take place.

Instructions and Explanation
The instructions and explanation for this scientific demonstration are found on pp. 92-93 of *Janice VanCleave's Chemistry for Every Kid*. Have the students complete the Lab Report on SW pg. 63.

Take it Further
Have the students observe a chemical reaction with cleaning power. You will need several dull, dirty pennies, a cup, and a can of dark cola soda. Place the pennies in the cup and pour the soda over them. Let the cup sit overnight. The next morning pour out the soda and observe the changes. (*The pennies should come out bright and shiny. This is because the phosphoric acid in dark cola reacts with the dirty, oxidized dull, top layer on the penny and returns it to bright and shiny!*)

Science-Oriented Books

Reading Assignments
- 📖 *Basher Science Chemistry pg. 41 Mole, pg. 82 Chemical Reaction* (**Note** – *If you choose to use only this resource with your students, you will need to share with them about the law of conservation of mass, which states that matter cannot be created or destroyed.*)
- 📖 *Usborne Science Encyclopedia pp. 76-77 Chemical Reactions*

(Optional) Additional topics to explore this week: *Basher Chemistry pg. 40 (Avogadro's number)*

Discussion Questions
After reading the selected pages, ask the following questions for your discussion time.

Chemical Reactions
- **?** What happens in a chemical reaction?
- **?** What are the reactants?
- **?** What are the products?

Conservation of Mass
- **?** What is the law of conservation of mass?

Moles
? What are moles?

? What do chemists use moles for?

(Optional) Additional Books

There are no additional books on the market for these topics. Instead, you can watch the following video on chemical and physical changes:

🖱 https://www.youtube.com/watch?v=BgM3e8YZxuc

Notebooking

Writing Assignments

☐ **Narration Page –** Have the students dictate, copy, or write one to four sentences on chemical reactions, conservation of mass, and moles on SW pg. 62.

☐ **(Optional) Lapbook –** Have the students complete the Reactions Mini-book on pg. 37 of *Chemistry for the Grammar Stage Lapbooking Templates*. Have the students cut out and fold the template. Have them color the picture on the cover. Then, have the students several sentences about what they have learned. Finally, glue the mini-book into the lapbook.

Vocabulary

The following definition is a guide. The students' definition does not need to match word for word.

✏ **Chemical Reaction –** An occurrence where the atoms in substances are rearranged to form new substances. (SW pg. 106)

Multi-week Projects and Activities

Unit Project

✂ **Chemical Changes Poster –** This week, have the students add a chemical reaction to the middle of their poster. Have them label the reactants side and the products side above the equation. Under the equation, have the students write the definition of a chemical reaction.

Projects for this Week

✂ **Coloring Pages –** Have the students color the following pages from *Chemistry for the Grammar Stage Coloring Pages*: Chemical Reactions pg. 32.

✂ **Chemical Reactions –** Have the students observe another chemical change by curdling milk. Add ¼ cup of vinegar to a clear glass or bowl. Then, add ¾ cup of milk and stir gently to mix. Wait fifteen minutes and observe the changes that have occurred. (*The acid in the vinegar causes the proteins to in the milk to bind up together, producing a chemical change that cannot be reversed.*)

✂ **Conservation of Mass –** Place a few ice cubes in a plastic cup and fill the cup ¾ of the way up with water. Use a maker to mark the water level and set the cup to the side. Keep checking the cup every hour until the ice completely melts to see how the water level changes. (*The students should see that the water level line doesn't change. This is due to the law of conservation of mass.*)

✂ **Mole Day –** Have a mole day celebration with you students. Traditionally, this would be done on June 23 or October 23, but you can celebrate Avogadro's number any day! Here are a few ideas you can use for your mole day celebration:

🖱 http://www.moleday.org/

Memorization

This week, begin working on memorizing the *Reactions* poem. (SW pg. 121)

Quiz

Weekly Quiz

⚑ "Chemical Changes Unit Week 2 Quiz" on SW pg. Q-26.

Quiz Answers

1. Reactants, Products
2. Stays the same
3. True
4. Answers will vary

Possible Schedules for Week 2

Two Days a Week Schedule

Day 1	Day 2
❑ Read about Chemical Reactions - pg. 76 (Chemical reactions) ❑ Add information about chemical reactions to the students' Narration Page ❑ Do the Scientific Demonstration: Green Pennies ❑ Define chemical reaction and reactive	❑ Read about Chemical Reactions - pg. 77 (Moles) ❑ Add information about conservation of mass and moles to the students' Narration Page ❑ Work on memorizing the *Reactions* poem ❑ Work on the Chemical Changes Poster ❑ Give the Chemical Changes Week 2 quiz

Five Days a Week Schedule

Day 1	Day 2	Day 3	Day 4	Day 5
❑ Do the Scientific Demonstration: Green Pennies ❑ Define chemical reaction and reactive ❑ Choose one or more of the additional books to read from this week	❑ Read about Chemical Reactions - pg. 76 (Chemical reactions) ❑ Add information about chemical reactions to the students' Narration Page ❑ Complete the Chemical Reactions Project	❑ Read about Chemical Reactions - pg. 77 sections on conservation of mass and equations ❑ Add information about conservation of mass to the students' Narration Page ❑ Complete the Conservation of Mass Project	❑ Read about Chemical Reactions - pg. 77 section on moles (Moles) ❑ Add information about moles to the students' Narration Page ❑ Have a Mole Day Party	❑ Give the Chemical Changes Week 2 quiz ❑ Work on the Chemical Changes Poster

All Week Long

❑ Work on memorizing the *Reactions* poem

Week 3: Types of Reactions Lesson Plans

Scientific Demonstration: Chemical Reactions in your Mouth

Supplies Needed
- ✓ Bread
- ✓ Iodine
- ✓ Eyedropper
- ✓ Wax paper

Purpose
This demonstration is meant to help the students see an important chemical reaction that occurs every day in their mouths.

Instructions and Explanation
The instructions and explanation for this scientific demonstration are found on pp. 108-109 of *Janice VanCleave's Chemistry for Every Kid.* Have the students complete the Lab Report on SW pg. 65.

Take it Further
Have the students use a chemical reaction to write a secret message. The instructions and explanation for this scientific demonstration are found on pp. 110-111 of *Janice VanCleave's Chemistry for Every Kid.*

Science-Oriented Books

Reading Assignments
- 📖 *Basher Science Chemistry pg. 90 Catalyst, pg. 91 Enzyme (**Note** – If you choose to use only this resource with your students, you will need to also read the definitions for endothermic and exothermic reactions from the glossary.)*
- 📖 *Usborne Science Encyclopedia pp. 78-79 Chemical Reactions, part 2*

(Optional) Additional topics to explore this week: *Basher Chemistry pg. 88 (Activation energy, Precipitate)*

Discussion Questions
After reading the selected pages, ask the following questions for your discussion time.

Types of Reactions
- ? What is an endothermic reaction?
- ? What is an exothermic reaction?
- ? What is another type of reaction?

Catalysts and Enzymes
- ? What is a catalyst?
- ? What is an enzyme?

(Optional) Additional Books

There are no additional books on the market for these topics. Instead, you can watch the following video on catalysts:

🖱 https://www.youtube.com/watch?v=OttRV5ykP7A

Notebooking

Writing Assignments

☐ **Narration Page –** Have the students dictate, copy, or write one to four sentences on types of reactions and rates of reactions on SW pg. 64.

☐ **(Optional) Lapbook –** Have the students complete the Types of Reactions Sheet on pg. 38 of *Chemistry for the Grammar Stage Lapbooking Templates.* Have the students cut out the template. Have the students write several sentences about what they have learned about endothermic and exothermic reactions. Then, have them glue the sheet into the lapbook.

Vocabulary

The following definitions are a guide. The students' definitions do not need to match word for word.

🖉 **Catalyst –** A substance that speeds up a chemical reaction. (SW pg. 105)

🖉 **Enzyme –** A catalyst that speeds up a chemical reaction in living things. (SW pg. 108)

Multi-week Projects and Activities

Unit Project

✂ **Chemical Changes Poster –** This week, under the equation, have the students write the definition of a endothermic and exothermic reactions.

Projects for this Week

✂ **Coloring Pages –** Have the students color the following pages from *Chemistry for the Grammar Stage Coloring Pages*: Types of Reactions pg. 33.

✂ **Types of Reactions –** Have the students see an endothermic and exothermic reaction. You will need baking soda, vinegar, water, Epsom salts, two cups, and a thermometer. Pour a few tablespoons of vinegar in one of the cups and place the thermometer in the liquid. Now, add a teaspoon of baking soda and observe what happens. (*The temperature should rise as this reaction is endo̶exothermic.*) In the second cup, add several tablespoons of water and place the thermometer in the liquid. Then, add a teaspoon of Epsom salts and observe what happens. (*The temperature should go down as this reaction is endothermic.*)

✂ **Catalyst –** Have the students watch a catalyst in action through the elephant toothpaste reaction! You will need a plastic bottle, small bowl, warm water, yeast, hydrogen peroxide, and dish soap for this demonstration. In a small bowl, mix ¼ cup of warm water with about a tablespoon of yeast and set aside. Pour about ½ a cup of hydrogen peroxide into the plastic bottle and add several drops of liquid dish soap. Next, quickly add the yeast mixture and step back to watch the toothpaste form!

Memorization

🗣️ This week, begin working on memorizing the *Reactions* poem. (SW pg. 121)

Quiz

Weekly Quiz

🖊️ "Chemical Changes Unit Week 3 Quiz" on SW pg. Q-27.

Quiz Answers

1. Exothermic, Endothermic
2. False (*A catalyst can speed up or slow down a reaction.*)
3. Enzyme
4. Answers will vary

Possible Schedules for Week 3

Two Days a Week Schedule	
Day 1	**Day 2**
❑ Do the Scientific Demonstration: Chemical Reactions in your Mouth ❑ Define catalyst and enzyme ❑ Work on memorizing the *Reactions* poem	❑ Read about Chemical Reactions, part 2 (Catalysts, Enzymes) ❑ Add information about the types of reactions and catalysts to the students' Narration Page ❑ Work on the Chemical Changes Poster ❑ Give the Chemical Changes Week 3 quiz

Five Days a Week Schedule				
Day 1	**Day 2**	**Day 3**	**Day 4**	**Day 5**
❑ Do the Scientific Demonstration: Chemical Reactions in your Mouth ❑ Define catalyst and enzyme ❑ Choose one or more of the additional books to read from this week	❑ Read about Chemical Reactions, part 2 pg. 78 ❑ Add information about the types of reactions to the students' Narration Page ❑ Complete the Types of Reactions Project	❑ Read about Chemical Reactions, part 2 pg. 79 (Catalysts, Enzymes) ❑ Add information about the catalysts and enzymes to the students' Narration Page ❑ Complete the Catalyst Project	❑ Choose one or more of the additional books to read from this week ❑ Work on the Chemical Changes Poster	❑ Give the Chemical Changes Week 3 quiz
All Week Long				
❑ Work on memorizing the *Reactions* poem				

Week 4: Oxidation and Reduction Lesson Plans

Scientific Demonstration: Browning

Supplies Needed
- ✓ Apple
- ✓ Cotton ball
- ✓ Lemon juice

Purpose

This demonstration is meant to help the students see an oxidation reaction in action.

Instructions

1. Cut the apple in half.
2. Have the students dip the cotton ball in lemon juice and rub the juice all over one half of the apple.
3. Set the apple halves aside in a place where they won't be disturbed.
4. Have the students check the apple halves every hour over the next four hours and have them make observations about the changes.
5. Have the students observe what happens and write what they see on the Lab Report on SW pg. 67.

Results and Explanation

The students should see that the apple half with the lemon juice remains the same, while the plain apple half begins to brown. This browning is due to oxidation - the oxygen in the air begins to break down the cells in the apple, causing it to turn brown.

Take it Further

Have the students look at another oxidation reaction: rusting. The instructions and explanation for this scientific demonstration are found on pp. 88-89 of *Janice VanCleave's Chemistry for Every Kid.*

Science-Oriented Books

Reading Assignments

- 📖 *Basher Science Chemistry* - pg. 86 Combustion (**Note** - *If you choose to use only this resource with your students, you will need to also read the definitions for oxidation and reduction from the glossary.)*
- 📖 *Usborne Science Encyclopedia pp. 80-81 Oxidation and Reduction*

(Optional) Additional topics to explore this week: *Basher Chemistry pg. 89 (Fireworks)*

Discussion Questions

After reading the selected pages, ask the following questions for your discussion time.

Oxidation

? What is oxidation?

? What happens during combustion?

Reduction

? What is reduction?

? What happens during photosynthesis?

(Optional) Additional Books

There are no additional books on the market for these topics. Instead, you can watch the following video on oxidation and reduction:

🖱 https://www.youtube.com/watch?v=NaGQ9VI5mwg

Notebooking

Writing Assignments

☐ **Narration Page** – Have the students dictate, copy, or write one to four sentences on oxidation and reduction on SW pg. 66.

☐ **(Optional) Lapbook** – Have the students complete the Oxidation and Reduction wheel-book on pg. 39 of *Chemistry for the Grammar Stage Lapbooking Templates*. Have them cut along the solid lines, punch a hole in the center, and use a brad fastener to fasten the two circles together. Have the students write several sentences about what they have learned about oxidation and reduction reactions. Finally, have them glue their mini-book into the lapbook.

Vocabulary

The following definition is a guide. The students' definitions do not need to match word for word.

✎ **Redox Reaction** – A chemical reaction that involves the transfer of electrons. (SW pg. 114)

Multi-week Projects and Activities

Unit Project

✂ **Chemical Changes Poster** – This week, under the equation, have the students write the definition of oxidation and reduction reactions.

Projects for this Week

✂ **Coloring Pages** – Have the students color the following pages from *Chemistry for the Grammar Stage Coloring Pages*: Oxidation pg. 34, Reduction pg. 35.

✂ **Oxidation** – Have the students learn about the chemistry of fireworks by watching the following video:

🖱 https://www.youtube.com/watch?v=nPHegSulI_M

Then, afterwards, you can make fireworks in a jar, which is not exactly an example of an oxidation reaction, but it is much safer to do in your kitchen! You will need food coloring, oil, a fork, a shallow bowl, warm water, and a glass jar. Pour a bit of oil in a bowl and add a few drops of food coloring. Break the drops into tiny droplets with a fork.

Slowly add the oil mixture in a jar filled partway with water. Wait a moment and observe the fireworks!

✂ **Reduction –** Have the students use a reduction reaction to clean a tarnished (oxidized) piece of silver. You will need a tarnished silver item (jewelry or silverware), tongs, a bowl, aluminum foil, baking soda, and hot water. Cover the bottom of the bowl with aluminum foil and then sprinkle 1 tablespoon of baking soda over it. Add a cup of hot water and mix until the baking soda is dissolved. Now, use the tongs to place the tarnished silver item into the solution. Wait a minute or two. (*You will see bubbles form and you might smell a rotten egg scent.*) Then, use the tongs to take the item out and observe the changes. (*The students should see that the item is much cleaner. This is because a redox reaction occurs between the aluminum, baking soda, and the tarnish, which is caused by a sulfur compound. This reaction removes the tarnish from the silver. Once the silver is exposed to the air again, sulfur in the air will cause another redox reaction, which produces the tarnish we see.*)

Memorization

This week, begin working on memorizing the *Reactions* poem. (SW pg. 121)

Quiz

Weekly Quiz
↳ "Chemical Changes Unit Week 4 Quiz" on SW pg. Q-28.

Quiz Answers
1. True
2. Oxidation
3. Reduction
4. Answers will vary

Possible Schedules for Week 4

Two Days a Week Schedule

Day 1	Day 2
❑ Do the Scientific Demonstration: Browning ❑ Define redox reaction ❑ Work on memorizing the *Reactions* poem	❑ Read about Oxidation and Reduction (Combustion) ❑ Add information about oxidation and reduction to the students' Narration Page ❑ Work on the Chemical Changes Poster ❑ Give the Chemical Changes Week 4 quiz

Five Days a Week Schedule

Day 1	Day 2	Day 3	Day 4	Day 5
❑ Do the Scientific Demonstration: Browning ❑ Define redox reaction ❑ Choose one or more of the additional books to read from this week	❑ Read about Oxidation and Reduction pg. 80 (Combustion) ❑ Add information about oxidation to the students' Narration Page ❑ Complete the Oxidation Project	❑ Read about Oxidation and Reduction pg. 81 ❑ Add information about reduction to the students' Narration Page ❑ Complete the Reduction Project	❑ Choose one or more of the additional books to read from this week ❑ Work on the Chemical Changes Poster	❑ Give the Chemical Changes Week 4 quiz

All Week Long

❑ Work on memorizing the *Reactions* poem

Chemistry for the Grammar Stage

Mixtures Unit

Mixtures Unit Overview
(4 weeks)

Books Scheduled

Encyclopedias
- *Basher Science Chemistry*
  OR
- *Usborne Science Encyclopedia*

Scientist Study Book
- *Pasteur's Fight Against Microbes*

Scientific Demonstrations Book
- *JVC Chemistry for Every Kid*

Sequence for Study
- **Week 1:** Mixtures
- **Week 2:** Separating Mixtures
- **Week 3:** Crystals
- **Week 4:** Scientist Study - Louis Pasteur

Mixtures Poem to Memorize

Mixtures, Solutions, Oh My!
A mixture occurs when two things combine
Like in air, Kool-Aid, and a salty brine

A solid and liquid together mix
And form a solution - a mixture trick

One separates a mixture many ways
Filter, distill, evaporate - some stays

Through chromatography, people can see
Ink separate into colors with glee

Supplies Needed for the Unit

Week	Supplies needed
1	Clear glass, Toothpick, Powdered fruit drink, Water

2	Black water soluble pen, Coffee filter, Saucer, Paper clip
3	Glass jar, Pencil, Pipe cleaners, Borax, Hot water
4	*No supplies needed.*

Unit Vocabulary

1. **Mixture** – A combination of two or more elements that are not chemically bonded together.
2. **Solution** – A mixture that consists of a substance dissolved in a liquid.
3. **Chromatography** – A method of separating the substances in a mixture by the rate they move through or along a medium, such as filter paper.
4. **Crystal** – A solid substance with a definite geometrical shape, straight edges and flat surfaces; hard, glassy-looking objects made of minerals.

Week 1: Mixtures Lesson Plans

Scientific Demonstration: Streamers of Color

Supplies Needed
- ✓ Clear glass
- ✓ Toothpick
- ✓ Powdered fruit drink
- ✓ Water

Purpose
This demonstration is meant to help the students see how a substance is dissolved in a liquid.

Instructions and Explanation
The instructions and explanation for this scientific demonstration are found on pp. 148-149 of *Janice VanCleave's Chemistry for Every Kid*. Have the students complete the Lab Report on SW pg. 73.

Take it Further
Have the students compare the different strengths of solutions. The instructions and explanation for this scientific demonstration are found on pp. 160-161 of *Janice VanCleave's Chemistry for Every Kid*.

Science-Oriented Books

Reading Assignments
- 📖 *Basher Science Chemistry pg. 21 Mixture*
- 📖 *Usborne Science Encyclopedia pp. 58-59 Mixtures*

(Optional) Additional topics to explore this week: *There are no additional topics for this week.*

Discussion Questions
After reading the selected pages, ask the following questions for your discussion time.

Mixtures
- **?** What is a mixture?
- **?** What are some examples of mixtures?
- **?** What is a solute? A solvent?

Mixing Liquids
- **?** What does it mean when two liquids are miscible? Immiscible?
- **?** What is an emulsion?

(Optional) Additional Books
- 📖 *Compounds and Mixtures (Explorer Library: Science Explorer)* by Charnan Simon
- 📖 *Mixtures and Solutions (Why Chemistry Matters)* by Molly Aloian

📖 *Mix It Up! Solution or Mixture?* by Tracy Nelson Maurer

📖 *Mixtures and Solutions (Building Blocks of Matter)* by Richard Spilsbury and Louise Spilsbury

Notebooking

Writing Assignments

☐ **Narration Page** – Have the students dictate, copy, or write one to four sentences on mixtures and mixing liquids on SW pg. 72.

☐ **(Optional) Lapbook** – Have the students begin the Mixtures lapbook by cutting out and coloring the cover on pg. 41.

☐ **(Optional) Lapbook** – Have the students complete the Mixtures Mini-book on pg. 42 of *Chemistry for the Grammar Stage Lapbooking Templates*. Have them cut out and fold the templates. Have the students color the cover. Then, have the students write a sentence or two about mixtures on the inside. Finally, glue the mini-book into the lapbook.

Vocabulary

The following definitions are a guide. The students' definitions do not need to match word for word.

✏ **Mixture** – A combination of two or more elements that are not chemically bonded together. (SW pg. 111)

✏ **Solution** – A mixture that consists of a substance dissolved in a liquid. (SW pg. 115)

Multi-week Projects and Activities

Unit Project

✂ **Mixtures Poster** – Over the course of this unit, the students will make a poster showing what they have learned about mixtures. This week, have them write the definition of a mixture and add several pictures and names of mixtures they can find in their homes. (*This has been done for you in the SW on pg. 70.*)

Projects for this Week

✂ **Coloring Pages** – Have the students color the following pages from *Chemistry for the Grammar Stage Coloring Pages*: Mixtures pg. 36.

✂ **Mixing** – Have the students make a frozen solution - ice cream in a bag! You will need ½ cup of heavy cream, ½ cup of milk, 1 tablespoon of sugar, ½ teaspoon of vanilla, 1 quart size ziploc plastic bag, 2 cups of crushed ice, 1 gallon size ziploc plastic bag, and ½ cup of rock salt. Begin by adding the cream, milk, sugar, and vanilla to the quart size baggie, close it, and shake vigorously to mix well. Then, add the ice and rock salt to the gallon size baggie, mix well, and then nestle the quart size bag into the ice mixture. Seal the large baggie up tightly and begin shaking! (**Note**—*It will take about 10 to 15 minutes for ice cream to form. You can use a towel or oven mitt to hold the large baggie as you shake if it gets* *too cold to handle.*)

✂ **Mixing Liquids –** Have the students make an emulsion. You will need a water bottle, water, and oil. Pour about a cup of water into the bottle and a cup of oil. Then, seal the bottle tightly and observe how the two liquids remain separated. Now, have the students shake the bottle vigorously for one minute. Have them observe the emulsion that was created.

Memorization

🗣 This week, begin working on memorizing the *Mixtures, Solutions, Oh My!* poem. (SW pg. 122)

Quiz

Weekly Quiz

🔦 "Mixtures Unit Week 1 Quiz" on SW pg. Q-29.

Quiz Answers

1. True
2. Solid
3. Miscible, Immiscible
4. Answers will vary

Possible Schedules for Week 1

| Two Days a Week Schedule ||
Day 1	Day 2
❑ Read about Mixtures - pg. 58 (Mixture) ❑ Add information about mixtures to the students' Narration Page ❑ Do the Scientific Demonstration: Streamers of Color ❑ Define mixture and solution	❑ Read about Mixtures - pg. 59 ❑ Add information about mixing liquids to the students' Narration Page ❑ Work on memorizing the *Mixtures, Solutions, Oh My!* poem ❑ Work on the Mixtures Poster ❑ Give the Mixtures Week 1 quiz

| Five Days a Week Schedule |||||
Day 1	Day 2	Day 3	Day 4	Day 5
❑ Do the Scientific Demonstration: Streamers of Color ❑ Define mixture and solution ❑ Choose one of the additional books to read from this week	❑ Read about Mixtures - pg. 58 (Mixture) ❑ Add information about mixtures to the students' Narration Page ❑ Complete the Mixtures Project	❑ Read about Mixtures - pg. 59 ❑ Add information about mixing liquids to the students' Narration Page ❑ Complete the Mixing Liquids Project	❑ Choose one of the additional books to read from this week ❑ Work on the Mixtures Poster	❑ Give the Mixtures Week 1 quiz
All Week Long				
❑ Work on memorizing the *Mixtures, Solutions, Oh My!* poem				

Week 2: Separating Mixtures Lesson Plans

Scientific Demonstration: Rainbow Effect

Supplies Needed
- ✓ Black water soluble pen
- ✓ Coffee filter
- ✓ Saucer
- ✓ Paper clip

Purpose
This demonstration is meant to help the students see how the different colors in ink can be separated out.

Instructions and Explanation
The instructions and explanation for this scientific demonstration are found on pp. 154-155 of *Janice VanCleave's Chemistry for Every Kid*. Have the students complete the Lab Report on SW pg. 75.

Take it Further
Have the students look at another method of separating mixtures - centrifuging. The instructions and explanation for this scientific demonstration are found on pp. 162-163 of *Janice VanCleave's Chemistry for Every Kid*.

Science-Oriented Books

Reading Assignments
- 📖 *Basher Science Chemistry pg. 62 Filter, pg. 63 Distillation, pg. 66 Chromatography*
- 📖 *Usborne Science Encyclopedia pp. 60-61 Separating Mixtures*

(Optional) Additional topics to explore this week: *There are no additional topics for this week.*

Discussion Questions
After reading the selected pages, ask the following questions for your discussion time.

Filtration
- **?** What happens during filtration?
- **?** What is filtration used to separate?
- **?** What is decantation?

Chromatography
- **?** What happens during chromatography?
- **?** What is chromatography used to separate?
- **?** What is evaporation?

Distillation
- **?** What happens during distillation?

? What is distillation used to separate?

? What is centrifuging?

(Optional) Additional Books

- 📖 *Mixing and Separating (Changing Materials)* by Chris Oxlade
- 📖 *Mixtures and Compounds (Internet-linked Library of Science)* by Alastair Smith and P. Clarke

Notebooking

Writing Assignments

- ☐ **Narration Page** – Have the students dictate, copy, or write one to four sentences on filtration, chromatography, and distillation on SW pg. 74.
- ☐ **(Optional) Lapbook** – Have the students complete the Separating Mixtures Flap-book on pp. 43-44 of *Chemistry for the Grammar Stage Lapbooking Templates*. Have the students cut out the sheets. Have them color the pictures on each sheet. Then, have the students write several sentences about what they have learned on the filtration, chromatography, and distillation sheets. Finally, glue the mini-book into the lapbook.

Vocabulary

The following definition is a guide. The students' definition does not need to match word for word.

- ✏ **Chromatography** – A method of separating the substances in a mixture by the rate they move through or along a medium, such as filter paper. (SW pg. 106)

Multi-week Projects and Activities

Unit Project

✂ **Mixtures Poster** – Have the students add a bit about the three methods for separating mixtures that they learned this week to the middle of their posters.

Projects for this Week

✂ **Coloring Pages** – Have the students color the following pages from *Chemistry for the Grammar Stage Coloring Pages*: Filtration pg. 37, Chromatography pg. 38, and Distillation pg. 39.

✂ **Filtration** – Have the students filter some dirty water. You will need dirty water, a funnel, a jar, a coffee filter, plus some sand and gravel. (**Note**—*You can easily make dirty water by adding some dirt, twigs, and/or leaves.*) Have the students set the funnel in the mouth of the jar and line it with the coffee filter, add a bit of sand, and then top it off with gravel. Next, have the students slowly pour the dirty water into their filter and watch what happens.

✂ **Chromatography** – Have the students use chromatography and markers to make some tie-dye art! The directions for this activity can be found here:

🖰 http://elementalscience.com/blogs/science-activities/120199363-marker-

> chromatography-art

✂ **Distillation** – Have the students watch the following video on separating a mixture of salt and water through distillation:

🖱 https://www.youtube.com/watch?v=N0f73tbGCRE

Memorization

🗣 This week, begin working on memorizing the *Mixtures, Solutions, Oh My!* poem. (SW pg. 122)

Quiz

Weekly Quiz

🗝 "Mixtures Unit Week 2 Quiz" on SW pg. Q-30.

Quiz Answers

1. Solids from liquids
2. False (*Chromatography is an excellent way to separate the colors in ink.*)
3. Liquids
4. Answers will vary

Possible Schedules for Week 2

Two Days a Week Schedule	
Day 1	Day 2
❑ Read about Separating Mixtures - pg. 60-61, sections on chromatography and evaporation (Chromatography) ❑ Add information about chromatography to the students' Narration Page ❑ Do the Scientific Demonstration: Rainbow Effect ❑ Define chromatography	❑ Read about Separating Mixtures - pg. 60-61, remaining sections (Filtration and Distillation) ❑ Add information about filtration and distillation to the students' Narration Page ❑ Work on memorizing the *Mixtures, Solutions, Oh My!* poem ❑ Work on the Mixtures Poster ❑ Give the Mixtures Week 2 quiz

Five Days a Week Schedule				
Day 1	Day 2	Day 3	Day 4	Day 5
❑ Do the Scientific Demonstration: Rainbow Effect ❑ Define chromatography ❑ Choose one or more of the additional books to read from this week	❑ Read about Separating Mixtures - pg. 60, sections on decantation and filtration (Filtration) ❑ Add information about filtration to the students' Narration Page ❑ Complete the Filtration Project	❑ Read about Separating Mixtures - pg. 60-61, sections on chromatography and evaporation (Chromatography) ❑ Add information about chromatography to the students' Narration Page ❑ Complete the Chromatography Project	❑ Read about Separating Mixtures - pg. 61, remaining sections (Distillation) ❑ Add information about distillation to the students' Narration Page ❑ Complete the Distillation Project	❑ Give the Mixtures Week 2 quiz ❑ Work on the Mixtures Poster
All Week Long ❑ Work on memorizing the *Mixtures, Solutions, Oh My!* poem				

Week 3: Crystals Lesson Plans

Scientific Demonstration: Crystalline Shapes

Supplies Needed
- ✓ Glass jar
- ✓ Pencil
- ✓ Pipe cleaners
- ✓ Borax (**Note**—*You will need about a quarter to a half of a cup of Borax for this demonstration. You can find Borax in the laundry aisle of the local grocery store – be sure to buy the one labeled laundry booster, not the soap that includes Borax.*)
- ✓ Hot water

Purpose
This demonstration is meant to help the students see the formation of crystals.

Instructions
1. Have the students shape the pipe cleaners into their desired shapes. (**Note**—*This can be as simple or as complex as they wish, but make sure it will fit through the opening of their jar.*)
2. Next, attach the shape to the pencil using another pipe cleaner. (**Note**—*You want the pencil to be able to rest on the edge of the jar without having the shape touch the sides or bottom of the jar.*)
3. Now, add hot water until it almost fills the jar, noting how many cups of water it takes to fill the jar.
4. Then, add the Borax, one tablespoon at a time, taking care each time to stir until the Borax is dissolved. (**Note**—*You want to add about 3 tablespoons of Borax for every cup of water added.*)
5. Finally, hang the shape in the jar so that it is completely covered by the liquid and allow the jar to sit undisturbed overnight.
6. The next morning, have the students observe what happens and write what they see on the Lab Report on SW pg. 77.

Explanation
The students should see that their shapes are covered with beautiful crystals. These were formed as the Borax came out of solution and attached itself to the pipe cleaners.

Take it Further
Have the students watch the formation of salt crystals. The instructions and explanation for this scientific demonstration are found on pp. 140-141 of *Janice VanCleave's Chemistry for Every Kid.*

Science-Oriented Books

Reading Assignments
- 📖 *Basher Science Chemistry* (**Note** - *There are no pages on crystals in this resource. If you choose to*

use only this resource with your students, you can read the definition for crystal structure from the glossary and choose one or more of the additional books to read.)

📖 *Usborne Science Encyclopedia pp. 90-91 Crystals*

(Optional) Additional topics to explore this week: *There are no additional topics to explore this week.*

Discussion Questions

After reading the selected pages, ask the following questions for your discussion time.

Crystals

? What are crystals?

? How do crystals form?

? How are crystals useful to us every day?

? What kind of crystals can we find in the earth's crust?

(Optional) Additional Books

📖 *Crystals (Rocks and Minerals)* by Connor Dayton

📖 *Growing Crystals* by Ann O Squire

📖 *What Are Crystals? (Let's Rock!)* by Molly Aloian

📖 *DK Eyewitness Books: Crystal & Gem* by R.F. Symes

Notebooking

Writing Assignments

☐ **Narration Page –** Have the students dictate, copy, or write one to four sentences on crystals on SW pg. 76.

☐ **(Optional) Lapbook –** Have the students complete the Crystals Hexa-book on pg. 45 of *Chemistry for the Grammar Stage Lapbooking Templates*. Have the students cut out the template. Have the students write several sentences about what they have learned about crystals. Then, have them glue the mini-book into the lapbook.

Vocabulary

The following definitions are a guide. The students' definitions do not need to match word for word.

✐ **Crystal –** A solid substance with a definite geometrical shape, straight edges, and flat surfaces. (SW pg. 106)

Multi-week Projects and Activities

Unit Project

✂ **Mixtures Poster –** Have the students add the definition of a crystal to the bottom third of their poster. Then, have them go on a crystal hunt to find crystals. Have the students take, cut out, or draw pictures of the crystals they find and add those to their poster.

Projects for this Week

✂ **Coloring Pages –** Have the students color the following pages from *Chemistry for the*

Grammar Stage Coloring Pages: Crystals pg. 40.

✂ **Crystal Hunt –** Have the students search the house for crystals. They can look for examples in jewelry, rock collections, and in the kitchen! The students can use the examples they have found on their mixtures poster.

✂ **Sugar Crystals –** Have the students make sugar crystals. You will need 3 cups of sugar, 1 cup of water, a jar, a pencil, string, foil, and a pot. Have the students tie the string to the pencil, so that it hangs just above the bottom of the jar. In the pot, mix the sugar and water and heat until the sugar is dissolved. Let the mixture cool a bit before pouring it into the jar. Cover with foil and set the jar in a place where it won't be disturbed for several weeks. Have the students observe the jar each day. When the crystals are big enough, usually about one to two weeks later, you can take them out, eat, and enjoy!

✂ **Alum Crystals –** Have the students make alum crystals. The directions for this project can be found in the "See for yourself" box on pg. 91 of the *Usborne Science Encyclopedia*.

Memorization

● This week, begin working on memorizing the *Mixtures, Solutions, Oh My!* poem. (SW pg. 122)

Quiz

Weekly Quiz

↳ "Mixtures Unit Week 3 Quiz" on SW pg. Q-31.

Quiz Answers

1. Cools off
2. True
3. False (*Crystals have straight edges and flat surfaces.*)
4. Answers will vary

Possible Schedules for Week 3

Two Days a Week Schedule	
Day 1	**Day 2**
❑ Do the Scientific Demonstration: Crystalline Shapes ❑ Define crystal ❑ Observe salt or sugar crystals with a magnifying glass ❑ Work on memorizing the *Mixtures, Solutions, Oh My!* poem	❑ Read about Crystals ❑ Add information about crystals to the students' Narration Page ❑ Work on the Mixtures Poster ❑ Give the Mixtures Week 3 quiz

Five Days a Week Schedule				
Day 1	**Day 2**	**Day 3**	**Day 4**	**Day 5**
❑ Do the Scientific Demonstration: Crystalline Shapes ❑ Define crystal ❑ Choose one or more of the additional books to read from this week	❑ Read about Crystals, part 1 pg. 90 ❑ Add information about crystals to the students' Narration Page ❑ Complete the Crystal Hunt Project	❑ Read about Crystals, part 2 pg. 91 ❑ Add information about crystals to the students' Narration Page ❑ Complete the Sugar Crystals Project	❑ Choose one or more of the additional books to read from this week ❑ Observe salt or sugar crystals with a magnifying glass ❑ Complete the Alum Crystals Project	❑ Give the Mixtures Week 3 quiz
All Week Long				
❑ Work on memorizing the *Mixtures, Solutions, Oh My!* poem				

Week 4: Scientist Study - Louis Pasteur

Science-Oriented Books

Reading Assignments

📖 *Pasteur's Fight Against Microbes by Beverly Birch and Christian Birmingham*

Over this week, the students will be reading *Pasteur's Fight Against Microbes*. You can purchase this book or you can get another book from the library. If you choose to get a different biography from the library, here are a few options:

📖 *Louis Pasteur: Founder of Modern Medicine* by John Hudson Tiner and Michael L. Denman
📖 *Germ Hunter: A Story about Louis Pasteur* by Elaine Marie Alphin and Elaine Verstraete
📖 *Louis Pasteur and the Fight Against Germs: Life Science* by Lisa Zamosky
📖 *Louis Pasteur: The Father of Microbiology* by Stephen Feinstein

If you cannot find a suitable book on Louis Pasteur at your library, you could look for a biography on one of the following scientists:

1. Marie Curie - She discovered the element radium.
2. Thomas Edison - He patented over 1100 inventions, among them the light bulb.
3. Alexander Fleming - He discovered penicillin.

Assign the reading according to each student's skill level. In other words, if the students need two weeks to read the biography, take the extra time by moving following weeks back and eliminating the additional biography assignment.

Discussion Questions

After reading the selected pages from the encyclopedias, ask the following questions in your discussion time:

? What was the title of the book you read?
? When and where was Louis Pasteur born?
? What was his major scientific contribution?
? List the events that surround his discovery.
? List some other interesting events in the his life.
? Why do you think that it is important to learn about Louis Pasteur?

Notebooking

Writing Assignments

☐ **Scientist Questionnaire** – Have the students fill in their answers to the questions about Louis Pasteur on SW pp. 78-79.
☐ **(Optional) Scientist Report** – If you have older students, you may opt to have them

write a short report on Louis Pasteur. Have the students use their responses on the scientist questionnaire to write their rough draft. It should include an introductory paragraph, a paragraph on his scientific contributions, a paragraph on other interesting events in the scientist's life, and a conclusion that includes why they feel it is important to study that particular scientist. Have the students proofread and correct mistakes. Finally, have them give their reports a title and rewrite them as a final draft. Here are a few ideas to make their reports a bit more interesting:

1. Have the students turn their reports into a mini-book on the scientist, including pictures they have drawn.
2. Have the students make posters to present their reports

Quiz

Weekly Quiz
- "Mixtures Unit Week 4 Quiz" on SW pg. Q-32.

Quiz Answers
1. Answers will vary

Chemistry for the Grammar Stage

Acids and Bases Unit

Acids and Bases Unit Overview
(4 weeks)

Books Scheduled

Encyclopedias
- *Basher Science Chemistry*

OR

- *Usborne Science Encyclopedia*

Scientific Demonstrations Book
- *JVC Chemistry for Every Kid*

Scientist Study Book
- *Marie Curie's Search for Radium*

Sequence for Study
- **Week 1:** Acids and Bases
- **Week 2:** pH
- **Week 3:** Salts
- **Week 4:** Scientist Study - Marie Curie

Acids and Bases Poem to Memorize

Acids and Bases
Acids dissolve in water to taste sour
Like the vinegar next to your flour

Bases break up into bitter compounds
Which can clean up stains left by coffee grounds

We measure their strength by the pH scale
Low for acids, High for base, tells the tale

But when we mix an acid and a base
Now, neutralization is what takes place

We see water and salt are left behind
A pH of 7 is what we find

Supplies Needed for the Unit

Week	Supplies needed
Unit Prep*	Strainer, Glass jar, Distilled water, Purple Cabbage, Coffee filters, Cookie sheet, Bowl, Scissors, Plastic bag
1	Lemonade, Cabbage indicator, Glass, Tablespoon
2	Cabbage paper, Paper, Eyedroppers, Vinegar, Ammonia, Jars
3	Vinegar, Baking soda, Water, Cabbage juice, Cabbage paper, 2 Clear cups, Eyedropper
4	*No supplies needed.*

*Unit Prep Note - For this unit, there are two supplies, cabbage indicator and cabbage paper, both of which you will need to make up ahead of time. The directions for making cabbage indicator can be found on pp. 190-191 of *Janice VanCleave's Chemistry for Every Kid*. The directions for making cabbage indicator can be found on pp. 192-193 of *Janice VanCleave's Chemistry for Every Kid*.

Unit Vocabulary

1. **Acid** – A chemical that dissolves in water and can neutralize a base. Weak acids taste sour.
2. **Base** – A chemical that dissolves in water and can neutralize an acid. Weak bases taste bitter.
3. **Indicator** – A substance that changes color in the presence of an acid or base.
4. **pH** – A scale from 0 to 14 used to measure the strength of acids and bases.
5. **Neutralization** – A reaction where one substance fully or partly cancels out another.
6. **Salt** – An ionic compound that when dissolved in water makes positive and negative ions. A salt is produced when you combine an acid and a base.

Week 1: Acids and Bases Lesson Plans

Scientific Demonstration: Drinkable Acid

Supplies Needed
- ✓ Lemonade
- ✓ Cabbage indicator (*See the unit prep note on pg. 153.*)
- ✓ Glass
- ✓ Tablespoon

Purpose
This demonstration is meant to help the students see that acids can be found in their kitchens.

Instructions and Explanation
The instructions and explanation for this scientific demonstration are found on pp. 200-201 of *Janice VanCleave's Chemistry for Every Kid*. Have the students complete the Lab Report on SW pg. 85. (**Note** - *You can have the students test other drinks in your refrigerator this week if they would like to do so.*)

Take it Further
Have the students see what test for the presence of a base. The instructions and explanation for this scientific demonstration are found on pp. 206-207 of *Janice VanCleave's Chemistry for Every Kid*. (**Note** - *This demonstration calls for tumeric paper; however, you can substitute the cabbage paper you already made. In the presence of a base, the cabbage paper will turn dark blue or green.*)

Science-Oriented Books

Reading Assignments
- 📖 *Basher Science Chemistry pg. 46 Acid, pg. 48 Bases*
- 📖 *Usborne Science Encyclopedia pp. 84-85 Acids and Bases*

(Optional) Additional topics to explore this week: *No additional topics scheduled.*

Discussion Questions
After reading the selected pages, ask the following questions for your discussion time.

Acid
- **?** What is an acid?
- **?** What is the difference between a strong and a weak acid?
- **?** What are some common acids?

Base
- **?** What is a base?
- **?** What is the difference between a strong and a weak base?
- **?** What are some common bases?

(Optional) Additional Books
- 📖 *Acids and Bases (Why Chemistry Matters)* by Lynnette Brent
- 📖 *Acids & Bases (Material Matters)* by Carol Baldwin
- 📖 *Acids and Bases (Chemicals in Action)* by Chris Oxlade

Notebooking

Writing Assignments
- ☐ **Narration Page –** Have the students dictate, copy, or write one to four sentences on acids and bases on SW pg. 84.
- ☐ **(Optional) Lapbook –** Have the students complete the Acids and Bases tab-book-book on pg. 46 of *Chemistry for the Grammar Stage Lapbooking Templates.* Have them cut out and color the pictures on the cover. Then, have the students write what they have learned about acids and bases on their respective tabs. Have them staple the mini-book together and glue it into the lapbook.

Vocabulary
The following definitions are a guide. The students' definitions do not need to match word for word.
- ✒ **Acid –** A chemical that dissolves in water and can neutralize a base. Weak acids taste sour. (SW pg. 104)
- ✒ **Base –** A chemical that dissolves in water and can neutralize an acid. Weak bases taste bitter. (SW pg. 105)

Multi-week Projects and Activities

Unit Project
- ✂ **Acids and Bases Poster –** Over this unit, the students will create two posters with the acids and bases they encounter. For example, this week, they could add lemonade to the acid poster and baking soda to the base poster. They can simply write the names or they can use pictures. (*This has been done for you in the SW on pg. 82.*)

Projects for this Week
- ✂ **Coloring Pages –** Have the students color the following pages from *Chemistry for the Grammar Stage Coloring Pages*: Acids pg. 41, Bases pg. 42.
- ✂ **Acids –** Have the students explore how acids affect baking. The instructions and explanation for this activity are found on pp. 202-203 of *Janice VanCleave's Chemistry for Every Kid.*
- ✂ **Bases –** Have the students see which cleaners in their houses contain bases. The instructions and explanation for this activity are found on pp. 210-211 of *Janice VanCleave's Chemistry for Every Kid.*
- ✂ **Neutralization –** Have the students neutralize an acid with a base. You will need vinegar, cabbage juice, baking soda, and a clear glass. Pour about a quarter of a cup of

vinegar into the glass and set it in the sink. Have the students add about a teaspoon of the cabbage juice, which should turn the solution a pinkish color. Then, add a tablespoon of baking soda and watch what happens! (*There should be a strong, bubbling reaction, which eventually calms down. The color of the solution should change to a neutral color, which is a bluish purple.*)

Memorization

🗣 This week, begin working on memorizing the *Acids and Bases* poem. (SW pg. 123)

Quiz

Weekly Quiz

🔖 "Acids and Bases Unit Week 1 Quiz" on SW pg. Q-33.

Quiz Answers

1. True
2. Vinegar, Lemon juice
3. False (*A base dissolves in water and can taste bitter.*)
4. Baking soda, Ammonia
5. Answers will vary

Possible Schedules for Week 1

Two Days a Week Schedule

Day 1	Day 2
❑ Read about Acids on pg. 84 (Acids) ❑ Add information about acids to the students' Narration Page ❑ Do the Scientific Demonstration: Drinkable Acids ❑ Define acid ❑ Work on memorizing the *Acids and Bases* poem	❑ Read about Bases on pg. 85 (Bases) ❑ Add information about bases to the students' Narration Page ❑ Define base ❑ Work on the Acids and Bases Posters ❑ Give the Acids and Bases Week 1 quiz

Five Days a Week Schedule

Day 1	Day 2	Day 3	Day 4	Day 5
❑ Do the Scientific Demonstration: Drinkable Acids ❑ Choose one or more of the additional books to read from this week	❑ Read about Acids on pg. 84 (Acids) ❑ Add information about acids to the students' Narration Page ❑ Complete the Acids Project	❑ Read about Bases on pg. 85 (Bases) ❑ Add information about bases to the students' Narration Page ❑ Complete the Bases Project	❑ Choose one or more of the additional books to read from this week ❑ Define acid and base	❑ Give the Acids and Bases Week 1 quiz ❑ Work on the Acids and Bases Posters

All Week Long

❑ Work on memorizing the *Acids and Bases* poem

Week 2: pH Lesson Plans

Scientific Demonstration: Acid-Base Testing

Supplies Needed
- ✓ Cabbage paper (*See the unit prep note on pg. 153.*)
- ✓ Paper
- ✓ Eyedroppers
- ✓ Vinegar
- ✓ Ammonia
- ✓ 2 Jars (add - JVC pg. 196-197)

Purpose
This demonstration is meant to help the students test for the presence of an acid or a base.

Instructions and Explanation
The instructions and explanation for this scientific demonstration are found on pp. 194-195 of *Janice VanCleave's Chemistry for Every Kid*. Have the students complete the Lab Report on SW pg. 87.

Take it Further
Have the students see how the concentration, or strength, of acid affects the indicator (cabbage juice) solution. The instructions and explanation for this scientific demonstration are found on pp. 196-197 of *Janice VanCleave's Chemistry for Every Kid*.

Science-Oriented Books

Reading Assignments
- 📖 *Basher Science Chemistry pg. 50 pH, pg. 52 Indicator*
- 📖 *Usborne Science Encyclopedia pp. 86–87 Acids and Bases, part 2*

(Optional) Additional topics to explore this week: *No additional topics scheduled.*

Discussion Questions
After reading the selected pages, ask the following questions for your discussion time.

pH
- **?** What does pH stand for?
- **?** What does a low pH, under 7, stand for?
- **?** What does a pH of 7 stand for?
- **?** What does a high pH, over 7, stand for?

Indicators
- **?** What is an indicator?
- **?** What is a universal indicator?

(Optional) Additional Books

There are no additional books on the market for these topics. Instead, you can watch the following videos on pH:

- 🖱 Importance of pH in everyday life: https://www.youtube.com/watch?v=x-nI3Ws7nxQ
- 🖱 What is the pH scale? https://www.youtube.com/watch?v=3U9n4BV2618

Notebooking

Writing Assignments

- ☐ **Narration Page** – Have the students dictate, copy, or write one to four sentences on pH and indicators on SW pg. 86.
- ☐ **(Optional) Lapbook** – Have the students complete the pH Scale Sheet on pg. 47 of *Chemistry for the Grammar Stage Lapbooking Templates.* Have the students cut out and write whether the section is acidic, basic, or neutral. Then, have the students color the acid range from dark (at 0) to light (before 7) red. Have them color the base section from dark (at 14) to light (before 7) blue. Have them leave the neutral section white. Finally, glue the sheet into the lapbook.

Vocabulary

The following definitions are a guide. The students' definitions do not need to match word for word.

- ✏ **Indicator** – A substance that changes color in the presence of an acid or base. (SW pg. 109)
- ✏ **pH** – A scale from 0 to 14 used to measure the strength of acids and bases. (SW pg. 113)

Multi-week Projects and Activities

Unit Project

- ✂ **Acids and Bases Poster** – This week, the students could add vinegar to the acid poster and ammonia to the base poster. They can simple write the names or they can use pictures. The students can also add information about the pH scale (i.e., what range of the scale is considered an acid or a base) to their posters.

Projects for this Week

- ✂ **Coloring Pages** – Have the students color the following pages from *Chemistry for the Grammar Stage Coloring Pages*: pH pg. 43.
- ✂ **pH** – Have the students create their own pH scale for cabbage juice indicator. You can view one in the following post:
  - 🖱 http://elementalblogging.com/science-corner-kitchen-acid-test/
- ✂ **Indicator** – Have the students use another indicator to test the acids and bases they know about so far. Grape juice is another option for an indicator. It turns reddish-purple in the presence of an acid and purplish-black in the presence of a base.

Memorization

🗣 This week, work on memorizing the *Acids and Bases* poem. (SW pg. 123)

Quiz

Weekly Quiz

🔦 "Acids and Bases Unit Week 2 Quiz" on SW pg. Q-34.

Quiz Answers

1. Power of hydrogen
2. pH 2 - acid, pH 7 - neutral, ph 10 - base
3. True
4. Answers will vary

Possible Schedules for Week 2

Two Days a Week Schedule	
Day 1	**Day 2**
❑ Do the Scientific Demonstration: Acid-Base Testing ❑ Define indicator and pH ❑ Work on the Acids and Bases Posters ❑ Work on memorizing the *Acids and Bases* poem	❑ Read Acids and Bases, part 2 (pH, Indicator) ❑ Add information about pH and indicators to the students' Narration Page ❑ Give the Acids and Bases Week 2 quiz

Five Days a Week Schedule				
Day 1	**Day 2**	**Day 3**	**Day 4**	**Day 5**
❑ Do the Scientific Demonstration: Acid-Base Testing ❑ Define pH and indicator ❑ Choose one or more of the additional books to read from this week	❑ Read about pH - sections and pH and acids in the soil on pg. 86 (pH) ❑ Add information about pH to the students' Narration Page ❑ Complete the pH Project	❑ Read about Indicators - sections on indicators and sulfuric acid on pp. 86-87 (Indicators) ❑ Add information about Indicators to the students' Narration Page ❑ Complete the Indicators Project	❑ Choose one or more of the additional books to read from this week ❑ Work on the Acids and Bases Posters	❑ Give the Acids and Bases Week 2 quiz
All Week Long				
❑ Work on memorizing the *Acids and Bases* poem				

Week 3: Salts Lesson Plans

Scientific Demonstration: Neutralize It

Supplies Needed
- ✓ Vinegar
- ✓ Baking soda
- ✓ Water
- ✓ Cabbage juice (*See the unit prep note on pg. 153.*)
- ✓ Cabbage paper (*See the unit prep note on pg. 153.*)
- ✓ 2 Clear cups
- ✓ Eyedropper

Purpose
This demonstration is meant to help the students see a neutralization in action.

Instructions
1. Pour about a quarter of a cup of vinegar in the glass and set it in the sink. Dip a strip of your cabbage paper into the vinegar to test to see if it is an acid. (*It should turn a pinkish color, indicating the presence of an acid.*)
2. In another cup, mix 1 tablespoon of baking soda with a half of a cup of warm water. Stir until dissolved. Dip a strip of your cabbage paper into the vinegar to test to see if it is an base. (*It should turn a bluish color, indicating the presence of a base.*)
3. Have the students add about a teaspoon of the cabbage juice to the cup in the sink, which should turn the vinegar solution a pinkish color.
4. Then, use the eyedropper to add the baking soda solution to the vinegar until the color changes to purple, indicating a neutral solution.
5. Have the students complete the Lab Report on SW pg. 89.

Explanation
When an acid and a base are mixed in the right proportions, the solution is neutralized. After some carbon dioxide is given off in the reaction, the solution now contains only water and a salt (sodium acetate) made from the acid and the base.

Take it Further
Have the students add drops of vinegar to see if they can turn the solution acidic once more. Then, have them do the same with the baking soda solution to see if they can turn the solution basic.

Science-Oriented Books

Reading Assignments
- 📖 *Basher Science Chemistry pg. 30 Ions (There are no new pages in this resource for this week.)*
- 📖 *Usborne Science Encyclopedia pp. 89-90 Salts*

📖 *"Neutralization" on Appendix pg. 190*

(Optional) Additional topics to explore this week: *No additional topics scheduled.*

Discussion Questions

After reading the selected pages, ask the following questions for your discussion time.

Neutralization

? What is neutralization?

? What happens when you mix an acid and a base?

Salts

? What is a salt?

? How can salts be formed?

(Optional) Additional Books

📖 *From Sea to Salt (Start to Finish, Second Series)* by Lisa Owings

📖 *The Story of Salt* by Mark Kurlansky and S. D. Schindler

Notebooking

Writing Assignments

☐ **Narration Page –** Have the students dictate, copy, or write one to four sentences on neutralization and salts on SW pg. 88.

☐ **(Optional) Lapbook –** Have the students begin the Neutralization sheet on pg. 48 of *Chemistry for the Grammar Stage Lapbooking Templates*. Have them cut out the sheet and label the pictures "acid", "base", and "water + salt". Then, have them glue the sheet into the lapbook.

Vocabulary

The following definitions are a guide. The students' definitions do not need to match word for word.

✐ **Neutralization –** A reaction where one substance fully or partly cancels out another. (SW pg. 111)

✐ **Salt –** An ionic compound that when dissolved in water makes positive and negative ions. A salt is produced when you combine an acid and a base. (SW pg. 115)

Multi-week Projects and Activities

Unit Project

✂ **Acids and Bases Poster –** This week, the students could add vinegar to the acid poster and baking soda to the base poster. They can simple write the names or they can use pictures.

Projects for this Week

✂ **Coloring Pages –** Have the students color the following pages from *Chemistry for the Grammar Stage Coloring Pages*: Neutralization pg. 44.

✂ **Neutralization –** Let the students have some fun with acids and bases by making some drinkable fizzing lemonade! The directions for this project can be found at the following blog post:

⌐ http://www.learnwithplayathome.com/2014/09/how-to-make-fizzing-lemonade-edible.html?m=1

✄ **Salt –** Have the students mix a tablespoon of vinegar and a teaspoon of baking soda together on a plate. Then, set the plate in a sunny place and observe what happens over the next several hours. (*The students should see that the liquid evaporates, leaving behind a white powder, which is the salt produced by the reaction, sodium acetate.*)

Memorization

● This week, work on memorizing the *Acids and Bases* poem. (SW pg. 123)

Quiz

Weekly Quiz

↳ "Acids and Bases Unit Week 3 Quiz" on SW pg. Q-35.

Quiz Answers

1. Water, salt
2. True
3. Ions
4. Answers will vary

Possible Schedules for Week 3

Two Days a Week Schedule	
Day 1	**Day 2**
❏ Read about neutralization from the Appendix ❏ Add information about neutralization to the students' Narration Page ❏ Do the Scientific Demonstration: Neutralize It ❏ Define neutralization ❏ Work on memorizing the *Acids and Bases* poem	❏ Read about Salts ❏ Add information about salts to the students' Narration Page ❏ Define salt ❏ Work on the Acids and Bases Posters ❏ Work on memorizing the *Acids and Bases* poem ❏ Give the Acids and Bases Week 3 quiz

Five Days a Week Schedule				
Day 1	**Day 2**	**Day 3**	**Day 4**	**Day 5**
❏ Do the Scientific Demonstration: Neutralize It ❏ Choose one or more of the additional books to read from this week	❏ Read about neutralization from the Appendix ❏ Add information about neutralization to the students' Narration Page ❏ Complete the Neutralization Project	❏ Read about Salts ❏ Add information about salts to the students' Narration Page ❏ Complete the Salts Project	❏ Choose one or more of the additional books to read from this week ❏ Define neutralization and salt	❏ Give the Acids and Bases Week 3 quiz ❏ Work on the Acids and Bases Posters
All Week Long				
❏ Work on memorizing the *Acids and Bases* poem				

Week 4: Scientist Study - Marie Curie

Science-Oriented Books

Reading Assignments

📖 *Marie Curie's Search for Radium by Beverly Birch and Christian Birmingham*

Over this week, the students will be reading *Marie Curie's Search for Radium.* You can purchase this book or you can get another book from the library. If you choose to get a different biography from the library, here are a few options:

📖 *Who Was Marie Curie?* by Megan Stine and Nancy Harrison
📖 *DK Biography: Marie Curie* by DK
📖 *Marie Curie (Giants of Science)* by Kathleen Krull
📖 *World History Biographies: Marie Curie: The Woman Who Changed the Course of Science* by Philip Steele

If you cannot find a suitable book on Marie Curie at your library, you could look for a biography on one of the following scientists:

1. Louis Pasteur - He revolutionized medicine and biology using chemistry.
2. Thomas Edison - He patented over 1100 inventions, among them the light bulb.
3. Alexander Fleming - He discovered penicillin.

Assign the reading according to each student's skill level. In other words, if the students need two weeks to read the biography, take the extra time by moving following weeks back and eliminating the additional biography assignment.

Discussion Questions

After reading the selected pages from the encyclopedias, ask the following questions in your discussion time:

? What was the title of the book you read?
? When and where was Marie Curie born?
? What was her major scientific contribution?
? List the events that surround her discovery.
? List some other interesting events in the her life.
? Why do you think that it is important to learn about Marie Curie?

Notebooking

Writing Assignments

☐ **Scientist Questionnaire** – Have the students fill in their answers to the questions about Marie Curie on SW pp. 90-91.

☐ **(Optional) Scientist Report** – If you have older students, you may opt to have them write a short report on Marie Curie. Have the students use their responses on the scientist questionnaire to write their rough draft. It should include an introductory paragraph, a paragraph on her scientific contributions, a paragraph on other interesting events in the scientist's life, and a conclusion that includes why they feel it is important to study that particular scientist. Have the students proofread and correct mistakes. Finally, have them give their reports a title and rewrite them as a final draft. Here are a few ideas to make their reports a bit more interesting:

1. Have the students turn their reports into a mini-book on the scientist, including pictures they have drawn.
2. Have the students make posters to present their reports

Quiz

Weekly Quiz
- "Acids and Bases Unit Week 4 Quiz" on SW pg. Q-36.

Quiz Answers
1.
2. Answers will vary

166

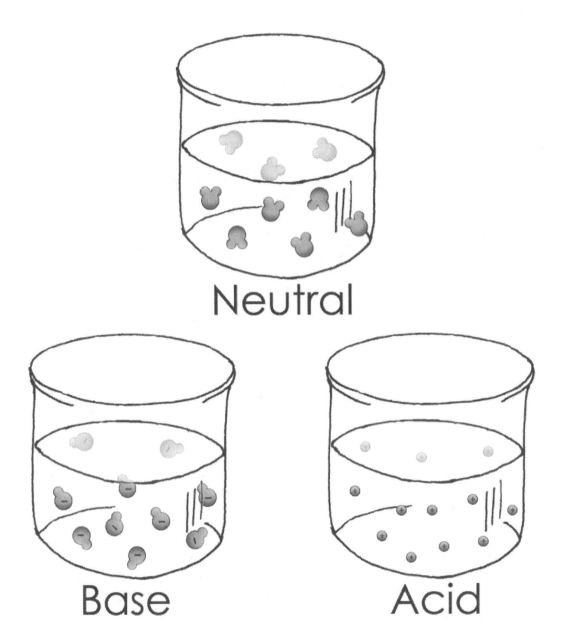

Chemistry for the Grammar Stage

Organic Chemistry Unit

Organic Chemistry Unit Overview
(4 weeks)

Books Scheduled

Encyclopedias
📖 *Basher Science Chemistry*
                OR
📖 *Usborne Science Encyclopedia*

Scientific Demonstrations Book
📖 *JVC Chemistry for Every Kid*

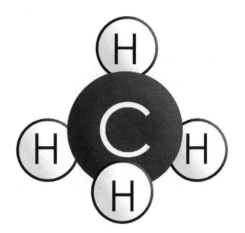

Sequence for Study
✎ **Week 1:** Organics Compounds
✎ **Week 2:** Alcohols & Esters
✎ **Week 3:** Hydrocarbons
✎ **Week 4:** Polymers and Plastics

Organic Chemistry Poem to Memorize

Organics
Organic chem is the science of life
Carbon and hydrogen bond without strife
These compounds help keep our bodies stable
But they can be made at the lab table
Alcohols have an OH group to boot
Esters make that sweet taste in gum or fruit
Hydrocarbons are in gas and oil
Polymers create a long-chained coil

Supplies Needed for the Unit

Week	Supplies needed
1	Construction paper, 6 Types of food (Cheese, Fruit, Yogurt, Chips, Muffin, Vegetable), Marker
2	Jar with lid, Rubbing alcohol, Cloves
3	Large clear glass bowl, Vegetable Oil, Water, Plastic spoon, Cotton balls, Polyester felt square
4	Vegetable oil, Cornstarch, Water, Food coloring, Plastic bag, Eyedropper

Unit Vocabulary

1. **Detergent** – A substance that enables water to remove dirt.
2. **Organic Compound** – A compound that contains the element carbon.
3. **Fermentation** – A chemical reaction that breaks down sugar into carbon dioxide and an alcohol.
4. **Polymer** – A substance with long-chain molecules, each made up of many small molecules called monomers.

Week 1: Organics Compounds Lesson Plans

Scientific Demonstration: Fat Test

Supplies Needed
- ✓ Construction paper
- ✓ 6 Types of food (e.g., Cheese, Fruit, Yogurt, Chips, Muffin, Vegetable)
- ✓ Marker

Purpose
This demonstration is meant to help the students see that fat is contained in some of the foods we eat.

Instructions
1. Have the students draw a grid with the marker on the sheet of construction paper. The grid should have six boxes with three across and two down.
2. Have the students set about a tablespoon of each food sample in each of the boxes in the grid and label the box with the type of food. Let the food sit there for 5 to 10 minutes.
3. Then, clean up and dispose of the food samples. Let the paper dry for 30 minutes to an hour.
4. Have the students observe the grid to look for stains that were left behind before completing the Lab Report on SW pg. 95.

Explanation
The results for this demonstration will vary, but basically students should see a stain on the paper where a food containing fat was put. This is because the paper absorbs the fat and fat does not evaporate like water will.

Take it Further
Have the students repeat the demonstration with a different group of food items.

Science-Oriented Books

Reading Assignments
- 📖 *Basher Science Chemistry pg. 68 Obnoxious Organics, pg. 74 Carboxylic Acids* (**Note -** *If you choose this resource, you will need to discuss detergents and soaps with your students.*)
- 📖 *Usborne Science Encyclopedia pp. 92, 94* (**Note -** *The scheduled pages for this week are a bit challenging, so you will only be reading short selections each day from the pages.*)

(Optional) Additional topics to explore this week: *Sections on "Unsaturated" and "Saturated" on USE pg. 93*

Discussion Questions
After reading the selected pages, ask the following questions for your discussion time.

Organic Compounds
? What are organic compounds?

? Where can we find organic compounds?

Organic Acids

? What is an organic acid?

? Where can we find organic acids?

Detergents

? What is a detergent? Soap?

? What do detergents do?

(Optional) Additional Books

- *Why We Need Fats (Science of Nutrition)* by Molly Aloian
- *Fats for a Healthy Body: For a Healthy Body (Body Needs)* by Heinemann

Notebooking

Writing Assignments

☐ **Narration Page** – Have the students dictate, copy, or write one to four sentences on organic compounds, organic acids, and detergents on SW pg. 94.

☐ **(Optional) Lapbook** – Have the students begin the Organic Chemistry lapbook by cutting out and coloring the cover on pg. 50.

☐ **(Optional) Lapbook** – Have the students begin the Organic Compounds Flap-book on pp. 51-52 of *Chemistry for the Grammar Stage Lapbooking Templates*. Have them cut out the cover and color the picture. Then, have the students cut out the tab for organic acids and write several sentences on with what they learned about organic acids for this week. Set the pages aside and save them for completion in week four of this unit.

☐ **(Optional) Lapbook** – Have the students complete the Detergents Mini-book on pg. 56 of *Chemistry for the Grammar Stage Lapbooking Templates*. Have the students cut out and fold the template. Have them color the picture on the cover. Then, have the students several sentences about what they have learned. Finally, glue the mini-book into the lapbook.

Vocabulary

The following definitions are a guide. The students' definitions do not need to match word for word.

✐ **Detergent** – A substance that enables water to remove dirt. (SW pg. 107)

✐ **Organic Compound** – A compound that contains the element carbon. (SW pg. 112)

Multi-week Projects and Activities

Unit Project

✂ There is no unit project for this unit.

Projects for this Week

✂ **Coloring Pages** – Have the students color the following pages from *Chemistry for the*

Grammar Stage Coloring Pages: Organic Compounds pg. 45, Detergents pg. 46.

✂ **Organic Compounds –** Have the students watch this video to learn the difference between organic and inorganic carbon compounds:

🖱 https://www.youtube.com/watch?v=7fv8GETEOu8

✂ **Organic Acids –** Have the students add the organic acids they learned about this week to their acid poster from the last unit.

✂ **Detergents –** Have the students observe the effects of a detergent. You will need a shallow bowl, liquid soap, and pepper. Fill the bowl with a thin layer of water and sprinkle pepper over the top. Then, add a drop of the liquid soap to the center of the bowl and watch what happens. (*The soap reduces the surface tension of the water and forces the pepper away from the center.*)

Memorization

👤 This week, begin working on memorizing the *Organics* poem. (SW pg. 124)

Quiz

Weekly Quiz

⚲ "Organic Chemistry Unit Week 1 Quiz" on SW pg. Q-37.

Quiz Answers

1. Carbon
2. True
3. Detergents
4. Answers will vary

Possible Schedules for Week 1

Two Days a Week Schedule

Day 1	Day 2
❑ Read about Organic Compounds - intro and organic compounds on pg. 92 (Organic Compounds)	❑ Read about Organic Acids and detergents - organic acids, types of acids, and detergents on pg. 94 (Carboxylic Acids)
❑ Add information about organic compounds to the students' Narration Page	❑ Add information about organic acids and detergents to the students' Narration Page
❑ Do the Scientific Demonstration: Fat Test	❑ Work on memorizing the *Organics* poem
❑ Define organic compounds and detergent	❑ Give the Organic Chemistry Week 1 quiz

Five Days a Week Schedule

Day 1	Day 2	Day 3	Day 4	Day 5
❑ Do the Scientific Demonstration: Fat Test ❑ Define organic compounds and detergent ❑ Choose one or more of the additional books to read from this week	❑ Read about Organic Compounds - intro and organic compounds on pg. 92 (Organic Compounds) ❑ Add information about organic compounds to the students' Narration Page ❑ Complete the Organic Compounds Project	❑ Read about Organic Acids - organic acids and types of acids on pg. 94 (Carboxylic Acids) ❑ Add information about organic acids to the students' Narration Page ❑ Complete the Organic Acids Project	❑ Read about Detergents - section on pg. 94 ❑ Add information about gases to the students' Narration Page ❑ Complete the Detergents Project	❑ Give the Organic Chemistry Week 1 quiz ❑ Review what you have learned so far this year

All Week Long

❑ Work on memorizing the *Organics* poem

Week 2: Alcohols and Esters Lesson Plans

Scientific Demonstration: Spicy Perfume

Supplies Needed
- ✓ Jar with lid
- ✓ Rubbing alcohol
- ✓ Cloves

Purpose
This demonstration is meant to help the students see how alcohol is a part of perfume-making.

Instructions and Explanation
The instructions and explanation for this scientific demonstration are found on pp. 172-173 of *Janice VanCleave's Chemistry for Every Kid*. Have the students complete the Lab Report on SW pg. 97.

Take it Further
Have the students create their own perfume using a concoction of different spices, dried herbs, or dried flowers.

Science-Oriented Books

Reading Assignments
- 📖 *Basher Science Chemistry pg. 72 Alcohol, pg. 76 Esters* (**Note** - *If you choose this resource, you will need to discuss fermentation with your students.*)
- 📖 *Usborne Science Encyclopedia pp. 94-95* (**Note** - *The scheduled pages for this week are a bit challenging, so you will only be reading short selections each day from the pages.*)

(Optional) Additional topics to explore this week: *No additional topics scheduled.*

Discussion Questions
After reading the selected pages, ask the following questions for your discussion time.

Alcohols
- **?** What are alcohols?
- **?** How are alcohols used?

Fermentation
- **?** What happens during fermentation?

Esters
- **?** What are esters?
- **?** How are esters used?

(Optional) Additional Books
There are no additional books on the market for these topics. Instead, you can watch the following video on fermentation:
- 👆 The Chemistry of Bread: https://www.youtube.com/watch?v=qylxpwNhFYI

Notebooking

Writing Assignments

- ☐ **Narration Page –** Have the students dictate, copy, or write one to two sentences on alcohols, fermentation, and esters on SW pg. 96.

- ☐ **(Optional) Lapbook –** Have the students work on the Organic Compounds Flap-book on pg. 53 of *Chemistry for the Grammar Stage Lapbooking Templates*. Have them cut out the sheet for alcohols and write several sentences on with what they learned about alcohols for this week. Set the pages aside and save them for completion in week four of this unit.

- ☐ **(Optional) Lapbook –** Have the students complete the Esters Mini-book on pg. 57 of *Chemistry for the Grammar Stage Lapbooking Templates*. Have the students cut out and fold the template. Have them color the picture on the cover. Then, have the students several sentences about what they have learned. Finally, glue the mini-book into the lapbook.

Vocabulary

The following definition is a guide. The students' definition does not need to match word for word.

- ✐ **Fermentation –** A chemical reaction that breaks down sugar into carbon dioxide and an alcohol. (SW pg. 109)

Multi-week Projects and Activities

Unit Project

- ✂ There is no unit project for this unit.

Projects for this Week

- ✂ **Coloring Pages –** Have the students color the following pages from *Chemistry for the Grammar Stage Coloring Pages*: Alcohols pg. 47, Esters pg. 48.

- ✂ **Alcohols –** Have the students use alcohol ink to paint on a slick surface, such as tile or glass. There are several ideas for this type of project in the following post:
  - 👆 http://truebluemeandyou.tumblr.com/post/128038875325/diy-alcohol-ink-glasses
  Note - *You can make your own alcohol ink by mixing a teaspoon of liquid dye, such as RIT dye, and a quarter of a cup of isopropyl alcohol.*

- ✂ **Fermentation –** Have the students use fermentation to make some fluffy rolls! Any recipe for yeast rolls will work, including the one found on the back of the yeast package.

- ✂ **Esters –** Have the students make an ester. You will need ethanol (denatured alcohol), sodium bisulfate (can be found at store that carries pool or wine-making supplies), and vinegar. Mix 3 teaspoons of ethanol with 2 teaspoons of sodium bisulfate. Then, add 3 teaspoons of vinegar and carefully smell the solution. (*The vinegar should have been replaced with the fruity scent of the ester that was made, ethyl acetate.*) **CAUTION** - Do not drink or touch the solution. When you dispose of the solution, be sure to flush it down with plenty of water.

Memorization

🗣 This week, begin working on memorizing the *Organics* poem. (SW pg. 124)

Quiz

Weekly Quiz

📌 "Organic Chemistry Unit Week 2 Quiz" on SW pg. Q-38.

Quiz Answers

1. Carbon, Hydrogen, Oxygen
2. False (*Fermentation is a chemical reaction that produces alcohol.*)
3. Smell
4. Answers will vary

Possible Schedules for Week 2

Two Days a Week Schedule	
Day 1	**Day 2**
❑ Read about Esters on pg. 95 (Esters) ❑ Add information about esters to the students' Narration Page ❑ Do the Scientific Demonstration: Spicy Perfume ❑ Define fermentation	❑ Read about Alcohols and Fermentation - alcohols and fermentation on pg. 94 (Alcohols) ❑ Add information about alcohols and fermentation to the students' Narration Page ❑ Work on memorizing the *Organics* poem ❑ Give the Organic Chemistry Week 2 quiz

Five Days a Week Schedule				
Day 1	**Day 2**	**Day 3**	**Day 4**	**Day 5**
❑ Do the Scientific Demonstration: Spicy Perfume ❑ Define fermentation ❑ Choose one or more of the additional books to read from this week	❑ Read about Alcohols - alcohols on pg. 94 (Alcohols) ❑ Add information about alcohols to the students' Narration Page ❑ Complete the Alcohols Project	❑ Read about Fermentation - fermentation on pg. 94 ❑ Add information about fermentation to the students' Narration Page ❑ Complete the Fermentation Project	❑ Read about Esters on pg. 95 (Esters) ❑ Add information about esters to the students' Narration Page ❑ Complete the Esters Project	❑ Give the Organic Chemistry Week 2 quiz ❑ Review what you have learned so far this year
All Week Long				
❑ Work on memorizing the *Organics* poem				

Week 3: Hydrocarbons Lesson Plans

Scientific Demonstration: Oily Clean-up

Supplies Needed
- ✓ Large clear glass bowl
- ✓ Vegetable Oil
- ✓ Water
- ✓ Plastic spoon
- ✓ Cotton balls
- ✓ Polyester felt square

Purpose
This demonstration is meant to help the students see what materials can be used to clean up an oil spill.

Instructions
1. Fill the bowl a halfway with water and add a half of a cup of oil to create a layer of oil sitting on top of the water.
2. Have the students choose one of the materials (spoon, cotton balls, or polyester felt) with which to soak or scoop up the oil. Have them record the results of their efforts on the Lab Report on SW pg. 99.
3. Then, have the students repeat the procedure from step 2 with the remaining two materials.
4. After they are done, have the students complete the Lab Report.

Explanation
The students should see that the plastic spoon and polyester felt worked the best to clean up the oil. This is because both these materials are attracted to the oil, since they are also non-polar, and they allow you to scoop up the oil rather than dab it away.

Take it Further
Have the students make a polypropylene scoop and then repeat the demonstration. To make the boom cleaner, you will need a polypropylene cloth sock or glove liners and a bit of wire. Use the wire to create a stiff "O" at the opening of the sock or glove liner. Then, use the scoop you have created to clean up the oil. (*This scoop is very similar to the boom-cleaner used to clean-up large scale oil spills in the environment.*)

Science-Oriented Books

Reading Assignments
- 📖 *Basher Science Chemistry pg. 70 Hydrocarbons*
- 📖 *Usborne Science Encyclopedia pp. 98-99 Crude Oil*

(Optional) Additional topics to explore this week: *Alkanes and Alkenes (USE)*

Discussion Questions

After reading the selected pages, ask the following questions for your discussion time.

Hydrocarbons

? What is crude oil?

? What is fractional distillation?

? Name several of the compounds that can be made from crude oil.

(Optional) Additional Books

- *Oil Spill! (Let's-Read-and-Find-Out Science)* by Melvin Berger and Paul Mirocha
- *Using Coal, Oil, and Gas (Exploring Earth's Resources)* by Sharon Katz Cooper
- *From Oil to Gas (Start to Finish, Second Series: Everyday Products)* by Shannon Zemlicka
- *Finding Out About Coal, Oil, and Natural Gas* by Matt Doeden

Notebooking

Writing Assignments

- ☐ **Narration Page –** Have the students dictate, copy, or write three to six sentences on hydrocarbons on SW pg. 98.
- ☐ **(Optional) Lapbook –** Have the students work on the Organic Compounds Flap-book on pg. 54 of *Chemistry for the Grammar Stage Lapbooking Templates*. Have them cut out the sheet for hydrocarbons and write several sentences on with what they learned about hydrocarbons for this week. Set the pages aside and save them for completion in week four of this unit.

Vocabulary

There are no vocabulary words for this week.

Multi-week Projects and Activities

Unit Project

✂ There is no unit project for this unit.

Projects for this Week

✂ **Coloring Pages –** Have the students color the following pages from *Chemistry for the Grammar Stage Coloring Pages*: Hydrocarbons pg. 49.

✂ **Oil Spill –** Have the students learn see the effects oil spills have on animals. You will need two feathers, vegetable oil, water, and dish soap for this activity. Begin by having the students dip the two feathers into the oil to coat them completely. Then, have them try to rinse the oil off one of the feathers with just water. Next, have them rub a bit of dish soap on the other feather until it lathers up. Then, rinse that feather off with water. Set both feathers on a paper towel to try. After about an hour, observe the changes to see which feather had the most oil removed from it. (*The students should see that the feather that was washed with the dish soap had the most oil removed. This is because the soap captures more of the oil so that it can be removed by the water.*)

✂ **Accidental Discoveries Video –** Have the students watch the following video about an accidental discoveries relating to coal tar, a byproduct of crude oil, and other hydrocarbons:

🖰 https://www.youtube.com/watch?v=Xowen_a787Y

Memorization

🔊 This week, begin working on memorizing the *Organics* poem. (SW pg. 124)

Quiz

Weekly Quiz

🖊 "Organic Chemistry Unit Week 3 Quiz" on SW pg. Q-39.

Quiz Answers

1. True
2. All the chemicals should be circled.
3. Fractional distillation
4. Answers will vary

Possible Schedules for Week 3

Two Days a Week Schedule	
Day 1	**Day 2**
❑ Do the Scientific Demonstration: Oily Clean-up ❑ Complete the Oil Spill Project ❑ Work on memorizing the *Organics* poem	❑ Read about Crude Oil (Hydrocarbons) ❑ Add information about hydrocarbons to the students' Narration Page ❑ Work on memorizing the *Organics* poem ❑ Give the Organic Chemistry Week 3 quiz

Five Days a Week Schedule				
Day 1	**Day 2**	**Day 3**	**Day 4**	**Day 5**
❑ Do the Scientific Demonstration: Oily Clean-up ❑ Choose one or more of the additional books to read from this week	❑ Read about Crude Oil on pg. 97 (Hydrocarbons) ❑ Add information about hydrocarbons to the students' Narration Page ❑ Complete the Oil Spill Project	❑ Read about Crude Oil on pg. 98 ❑ Add information about hydrocarbons to the students' Narration Page ❑ Watch the Accidental Discoveries Video	❑ Choose one or more of the additional books to read from this week ❑ Review what you have learned so far this year	❑ Give the Organic Chemistry Week 3 quiz
All Week Long				
❑ Work on memorizing the *Organics* poem				

Week 4: Polymers and Plastics Lesson Plans

Scientific Demonstration: Kitchen Plastic

Supplies Needed

- ✓ Vegetable oil
- ✓ Cornstarch
- ✓ Water
- ✓ Food coloring
- ✓ Plastic bag
- ✓ Eyedropper

Purpose

This demonstration is meant to help the students see that they can make a plastic from the materials in your kitchen.

Instructions

1. In the bag, mix 3 tablespoons of cornstarch, 3 tablespoons of water, 8 to 10 drops of vegetable oil, and a few drops of food coloring.
2. Have the students mix the ingredients up thoroughly.
3. Then, seal the bag halfway, place it on a plate, and place the bag in the microwave on high for 25 to 30 seconds. (*The mixture should bubble a bit and become somewhat transparent.*)
4. Use a hot mitt to remove the baggie and let it cool for a bit.
5. Once it is cool enough to handle, you can shape the plastic into what the students desire. Then, let it sit overnight to completely harden.
6. Have the students complete the Lab Report on SW pg. 101.

Explanation

The students should see that have created a soft moldable plastic that hardens when left overnight. As the cornstarch heats up, it reacts with the water and oil to create a polymer, which is the basic of plastics.

Take it Further

Have the students make a different kind of bioplastic using milk and vinegar. The directions for this can be found at the following website:

✒ https://sciencebob.com/make-plastic-milk/

Science-Oriented Books

Reading Assignments

- 📖 *Basher Science Chemistry pg. 35 Polymer* (**Note -** *If you choose this resource, you will need to discuss plastics with your students.*)
- 📖 *Usborne Science Encyclopedia pp. 101–102 Polymers and Plastics*

(Optional) Additional topics to explore this week: *Using Plastics (USE)*

Discussion Questions

After reading the selected pages, ask the following questions for your discussion time.

Polymers

? What are polymers?

? What is the difference between synthetic and natural polymers?

? What is polymerization

Plastics

? What are the two groups of plastics?

? What can plastics be used for?

(Optional) Additional Books

- *Plastic (Everyday Materials)* by Andrew Langley
- *Plastic, Ahoy!: Investigating the Great Pacific Garbage Patch* by Patricia Newman and Annie Crawley
- *The Adventures of a Plastic Bottle: A Story About Recycling (Little Green Books)* by Alison Inches and Pete Whitehead
- *From Plastic to Soccer Ball (Start to Finish: Sports Gear)* by Robin Nelson

Notebooking

Writing Assignments

- ☐ **Narration Page –** Have the students dictate, copy, or write one to four sentences on polymers and plastics on SW pg. 100.
- ☐ **(Optional) Lapbook –** Have the students work on the Organic Compounds Flap-book on pg. 55 of *Chemistry for the Grammar Stage Lapbooking Templates*. Have them cut out the sheet for polymers and write several sentences on with what they learned about polymers for this week. Set the pages aside and save them for completion in week four of this unit.
- ☐ **(Optional) Lapbook –** Have the students finish their lapbook. Have them cut out and color the *Organics* poem on pg. 58 of *Chemistry for the Grammar Stage Lapbooking Templates*. Once they are done, have them glue the sheet into their lapbook.

Vocabulary

The following definition is a guide. The students' definitions do not need to match word for word.

- ✐ **Polymer –** A substance with long-chain molecules, each made up of many small molecules called monomers. (SW pg. 113)

Multi-week Projects and Activities

Unit Project

✂ There is no unit project for this unit.

Projects for this Week

✂ **Coloring Pages –** Have the students color the following pages from *Chemistry for the Grammar Stage Coloring Pages*: Polymer pg. 50, Plastic pg. 51.

✂ **Polymer –** Have the students make their own polymer slime. You will need white (or clear gel) glue, water, a plastic baggie, and some Borax (the laundry booster, not the laundry detergent.) Begin by mixing 4oz of glue with 4oz of water in a plastic bag. Next, in a separate cup, mix a quarter cup of water with half a teaspoon of Borax. Add the Borax solution to the baggie and massage the bag for a few minutes until a nice firm slime has formed. Then, pull the slime out of the baggie and let the students have fun with their polymer.

✂ **Plastic –** Have the students go on a hunt around the house to find what items are made of plastic. Then, have them create a collage displaying their results. They can draw, cut out, or take and paste the pictures of the items they find.

Memorization

🗣 This week, begin working on memorizing the *Organics* poem. (SW pg. 124)

Quiz

Weekly Quiz

🖊 "Organic Chemistry Unit Week 4 Quiz" on SW pg. Q-40.

Quiz Answers

1. Short
2. True
3. Man
4. Answers will vary

Possible Schedules for Week 4

Two Days a Week Schedule	
Day 1	Day 2
❑ Do the Scientific Demonstration: Kitchen Plastic ❑ Define polymer ❑ Work on memorizing the *Organics* poem	❑ Read about Polymers and Plastics (Polymers) ❑ Add information about polymers and plastics to the students' Narration Page ❑ Work on memorizing the *Organics* poem ❑ Give the Organic Chemistry Week 4 quiz

Five Days a Week Schedule				
Day 1	Day 2	Day 3	Day 4	Day 5
❑ Do the Scientific Demonstration: Kitchen Plastic ❑ Define polymer ❑ Choose one or more of the additional books to read from this week	❑ Read about Polymers on pg. 100 (Polymers) ❑ Add information about polymers to the students' Narration Page ❑ Complete the Polymer Project	❑ Read about Plastics on pg. 101 ❑ Add information about plastics to the students' Narration Page ❑ Complete the Plastics Project	❑ Choose one or more of the additional books to read from this week ❑ Review what you have learned so far this year	❑ Give the Organic Chemistry Week 4 quiz
All Week Long ❑ Work on memorizing the *Organics* poem				

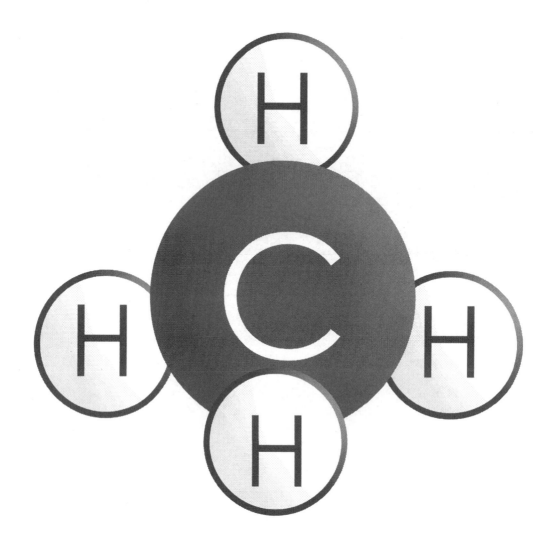

Chemistry for the Grammar Stage

Appendix

Polar and Non-polar Molecules

There are two different types of molecules – polar and nonpolar. In a nutshell, polar molecules have a charge, while nonpolar molecules do not.

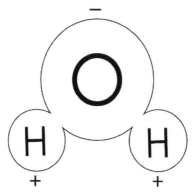

A polar molecule has two ends. Just like a magnet – one end of the molecule is positive, and the other end of the molecule is negative. Water is an example of a polar molecule. Polar molecules are attracted to other polar molecules.

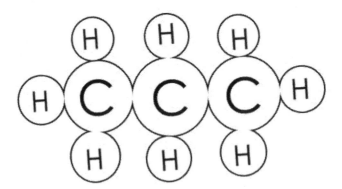

A nonpolar molecule does not have a positive or a negative end. These molecules are known as neutral molecules. Oil is an example of a nonpolar molecule. Nonpolar molecules are attracted to other nonpolar molecules.

In solutions, we say that like dissolves like. Polar molecules can dissolve other polar molecules. Nonpolar molecules can dissolve nonpolar molecules. Polar and nonpolar molecules do not dissolve in each other, which is why oil and water do not mix.

Transition Metal Hunt

21 Sc Scandium 44.96	22 Ti Titanium 47.87	23 V Vanadium 50.94	24 Cr Chromium 52	25 Mn Manganese 54.94	26 Fe Iron 55.85	27 Co Cobalt 58.93	28 Ni Nickel 58.69	29 Cu Copper 63.55	30 Zn Zinc 65.39
39 Y Yttrium 88.91	40 Zr Zirconium 91.22	41 Nb Niobium 92.91	42 Mo Molybdenum 95.94	43 Tc Technetium 98.91	44 Ru Ruthenium 101.07	45 Rh Rhodium 102.91	46 Pd Palladium 106.42	47 Ag Silver 107.87	48 Cd Cadmium 112.41
* 71 Lu Lutetium 175	72 Hf Hafnium 178.49	73 Ta Tantalum 180.95	74 W Tungsten 183.85	75 Re Rhenium 186.21	76 Os Osmium 190.2	77 Ir Iridium 192.2	78 Pt Platinum 195.08	79 Au Gold 196.97	80 Hg Mercury 200.59
** 103 Lr Lawrencium 262	104 Rf Rutherfordium 261.11	105 Db Dubnium 262.11	106 Sg Seaborgium 263.12	107 Bh Bohrium 264.1	108 Hs Hassium 265.1	109 Mt Meitnerium 266	110 Ds Darmstadtium [271]	111 Rg Roentgenium [272]	112 Cn Copernicium [277]

Many of the transition metals can be found in your house! Today, you are going to hunt around your home looking for some of the elements above. You can look anywhere you have permission to do so. (*Be sure to check the labels in your pantry and medicine cabinet as well!*) Here are a few ideas of items you can look for:

✓ Jewelry, which is often made from gold, silver, or platinum.
✓ Coins, which contain copper and nickel.
✓ Stainless steel, which is combination of iron, vanadium, nickel, tungsten, and more.
✓ Magnets are usually made from iron.
✓ Antiperspirant contains zirconium.
✓ Lightbulb filaments are made from tungsten.
✓ Bicycle frames are sometimes made of titanium.
✓ Anything with Vitamin B12, which contains colbalt.
✓ Fishing lures, which often contain lead.
✓ Hand tools are often coated with chrom-moly steel, which contains chromium and molybdenum.
✓ Diaper cream often contains zinc.
✓ Rechargeable batteries can contain both nickel and cadmium.

Neutralization

Neutralization is a chemical reaction that happens when an acid and a base cancel one another out. The end result in a neutral solution.

In water, acids like to donate hydrogen ions (H+). On the hand, bases in water like to donate hydroxide ions (OH-). The two ions are very attracted to each other. The hydrogen ion and the hydroxide ion come together to form something we are very familiar with – water!

There are other ions left in the solution after the acid donates its hydrogen ion and the base donates it hydroxide ion. These ions come together to form a salt.

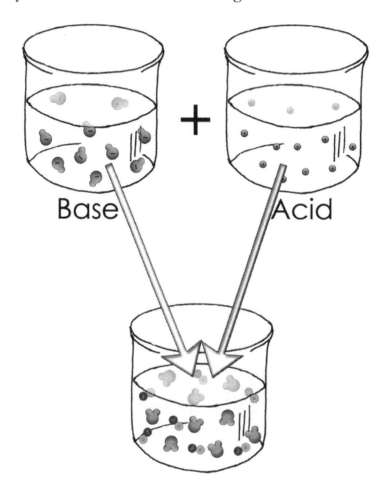

When you mix an acid and a base together in the right proportions, all of the ions will react and the solution will be come neutral.

Chemistry for the Grammar Stage

Glossary

192

A

- **Acid** – A chemical that dissolves in water and can neutralize a base. Weak acids taste sour.

- **Air** – A mixture of gases that form a protective layer around the Earth.

- **Alloy** – A mixture of two or more metals or a metal and a non-metal.

- **Atomic Mass** – The average mass number of the atoms in a sample of an element.

- **Atomic Number** – The number of protons in the nucleus of an atom.

B

- **Base** – A chemical that dissolves in water and can neutralize an acid. Weak bases taste bitter.

C

- **Catalyst** – A substance that speeds up a chemical reaction.

- **Chemical Bond** – A force that holds together two or more atoms.

- **Chemical Reaction** –An occurrence where the atoms in substances are rearranged to form new substances.

- **Chemical Symbol** – A shorthand way of representing a specific element in formulae and equations.

- **Chromatography** – A method of separating the substances in a mixture by the rate they move through or along a medium, such as filter paper.

- **Crystal** – A solid substance with a definite geometrical shape, straight edges and flat surfaces; hard, glassy-looking objects made of minerals.

D

- **Detergent** – A substance that enables water to remove dirt.

- **Diffusion** – The spreading out of a gas to fill the available space.

E

- **Electron** – A negatively charged particle in an atom.

- **Electron Shell** – The region around an atom's nucleus in which a certain amount of electrons can reside.

- **Elements** – A substance made up of one type of atom, which cannot be broken down by chemical reaction to form a simpler substance.

- **Enzyme** – A catalyst that speeds up a chemical reaction in living things.

- **Essential Element** – An element that is essential to life on earth, such as carbon, hydrogen, nitrogen, and oxygen.

- **Evaporation** – The process by which the surface molecules of a liquid escape into a vapor.

F

- **Fermentation** – A chemical reaction that breaks down sugar into carbon dioxide and an alcohol.

G

H

- **Hard Water** – Water that contains a lot of dissolved minerals.

I

- **Indicator** – A substance that changes color in the presence of an acid or base.

- **Inert** – An element that is completely nonreactive.

- **Ion** – An atom or group of atoms that has become charged by gaining or losing one or more electrons.

- **Isotope** – An atom that has a different number of neutrons and so has a different mass number from the other atoms of an element.

J

K

L

M

- **Metal** – The largest class of elements; they are usually shiny and solid at room temperature.

- **Metalloid –** An element that shares some of the properties of metals and nonmetals.

- **Mixture –** A combination of two or more elements that are not chemically bonded together.

- **Molecule –** A substance made up of two or more atoms that are chemically bonded.

N

- **Neutralization –** A reaction where one substance fully or partly cancels out another.

- **Neutron –** A neutral particle in an atom.

- **Nonmetal –** A class of elements that can be non-shiny solids or gases.

O

- **Organic Compound –** A compound that contains the element carbon.

- **Oxidation –** A chemical reaction in which a substance combines with oxygen.

P

- **Periodic Table –** A systematic arrangement of the elements in order of increasing atomic number.

- **pH –** A scale from 0 to 14 used to measure the strength of acids and bases.

- **Physical Change –** A change that occurs in which no new substances are made.

- **Polymer –** A substance with long-chain molecules, each made up of many small molecules called monomers.

- **Proton –** A positively charged particle in an atom.

Q

R

- **Radioactive Decay –** The process by which a nucleus ejects particles through radiation to becoming the nucleus of a series of different elements until stability is reached.

- **Reactive –** The tendency of a substance to react with other substances.

- **Redox Reaction –** A chemical reaction that involves the transfer of electrons.

- **Refraction –** The bending of light as it passes through a different medium.

S

- **Salt** – An ionic compound that when dissolved in water makes positive and negative ions. A salt is produced when you combine an acid and a base.

- **Solution** – A mixture that consists of a substance dissolved in a liquid.

- **States of Matter** – The different forms in which a substance can exist: solid, liquid, and gas.

- **Sublimation** – A change from solid to gas without going through liquid form.

- **Surface Tension** – A force that pulls together molecules on the surface of a liquid.

T

U

V

- **Volume** – The space occupied by matter.

W

X

Y

Z

Chemistry for the Grammar Stage

General Templates

Project Record Sheet

Paste a picture of your
project in this box.

What I Learned:

_____

_____

_____

_____

_____

_____

_____

Two Days a Week Schedule

Day 1	Day 2
❑	❑
❑	❑
❑	❑
❑	❑
❑	❑
❑	❑

Things to Prepare

❑

❑

❑

Notes

Five Days a Week Schedule

Day 1	Day 2	Day 3	Day 4	Day 5
❑	❑	❑	❑	❑
❑	❑	❑	❑	❑
❑	❑	❑	❑	❑
❑	❑	❑	❑	❑

All Week Long

❑

❑

Things to Prepare

❑

❑

❑

Notes

Made in the USA
Columbia, SC
01 July 2021